Revise for Geography AS Edexcel Specification B

Dulcie Knifton

Heinemann

Inspiring generations

Heinemann Educational Publishers
Halley Court, Jordan Hill, Oxford OX2 8EJ
Part of Harcourt Education

Heinemann is the registered trademark of
Harcourt Education Limited

© Dulcie Knifton, 2004

First published 2004

09 08 07 06 05
10 9 8 7 6 5 4 3 2

British Library Cataloguing in Publication Data is available
from the British Library on request.

ISBN 0 435 10154 4

Copyright notice

Edited by Caroline Sinclair
Designed by hicksdesign
Typeset and illustrated by Saxon Graphics Ltd, Derby

Original illustrations © Harcourt Education Limited, 2004

Printed in the UK by Thomson Litho

Acknowledgements

Every effort has been made to contact copyright holders of material reproduced in this book.
Any omissions will be rectified in subsequent printings if notice is given to the publishers.

Websites

On pages where you are asked to go to www.heinemann.co.uk/hotlinks to complete a task
or download information, please insert code **1544S** at the website.

Contents

PART 3/ The environmental investigation

How to use this revision guide

Revise for Geography AS Edexcel Specification B is for the Edexcel Geography AS course, Specification B. It is divided into three modules.

Part 1 Changing landforms and their management

This module covers the *Changing landforms and their management* element of the AS Specification that makes up the 6471 exam. The two topics within this unit are *River environments* and *Coastal environments*.

Part 2 Managing change in human environments

This module covers the *Managing change in human environments* element of the AS Specification that makes up the 6472 exam. The two topics within this unit are *Rural environments* and *Urban environments*.

Part 3 The environmental investigation

This module gives advice on completing the write-up of the environmental investigation, the coursework component of the AS course.

Each Part introduces the module and gives an overview of all the topics to be covered. The content of each module is then divided into sections, e.g. 1.2 Soil moisture budgets. Each section includes:

- a list of what you will be revising
- a summary of the topic content
- indicates **key concepts** to learn
- provides helpful **Reminders**
- diagrams that highlight key information
- helpful case studies.

Every section also provides practice **Quick check questions** to help you test your understanding.

Where there are options within the specification, the most popular choices in each module have been covered in this guide, together with relevant summarised examples and case studies to support the key content and concepts.

Exam style questions and answers

At the end of each module there are longer end-of-module questions similar in style to those you will encounter in the module exams. Answers to these questions are provided at the end of the book.

Content of AS: the assessments

Edexcel (Specification B) AS Geography: Assessment

You can take an AS (Advanced Subsidiary) Level qualification on its own or as the first part of an A (Advanced) Level qualification. The AS Level currently forms 50 per cent of an A Level.

The AS Geography (Specification B) assessment is made up of the following components (see Table 1).

AS Geography (Specification B) components

Unit	Type of assessment	Format of assessment	Raw number of marks	AS weighting
1. Changing landforms and their management ○ River environments ○ Coastal environments	Module exam (6471) 1 hr 30 mins	5 questions. Students choose 3 questions. Each question is worth 30 marks: ○ 20 marks for short structured / data response questions ○ 10 marks for an extended writing question; often known as the 'mini essay'. Questions 1 and 2 focus on river environments; question 3 has a mixed rivers and coasts focus; and questions 4 and 5 focus on coastal environments.	90 marks (+ 4 for quality of written communication: QWC)	33.3 per cent
2. Managing change in human environments ○ Rural environments ○ Urban environments	Module exam (6472) 1 hr 30 mins	5 questions. Students choose 3 questions. Each question is worth 30 marks: ○ 20 marks for short structured / data response questions ○ 10 marks for an extended writing question; often known as the 'mini essay'. Questions 1 and 2 focus on rural environments; question 3 has a mixed rural and urban focus; and questions 4 and 5 focus on urban environments.	90 marks (+ 4 for QWC)	33.3 per cent
3. Environmental investigation	Individual coursework report based on fieldwork (6473) 2500 words maximum	A fieldwork investigation of a site or small-scale area linked to one of the environment studies at AS. Students are assessed on their ability to collect, represent and analyse primary and secondary data using a range of techniques, and to evaluate their findings and draw conclusions.	100 marks	33.3 per cent

Table 1 AS Geography (Specification B) components

This book is designed to help you prepare for all AS modules in the Specification B course. Good luck with your revision.

PART 1

Changing landforms and their management

This module covers the *Changing landforms and their management* element of the AS Specification that makes up the 6471 exam. Examples and case studies are included at relevant points. The two topics within this unit are River environments and Coastal environments:

River environments

- The hydrological cycle
- The impact of the hydrological cycle on soil moisture budgets, storm hydrographs and river regimes
- Processes of erosion, transportation and deposition
- River channel load and factors influencing sediment budgets, including the Hjulstrom curve
- Physical factors that influence channel characteristics and valley landforms
- Hydraulic geometry and downstream changes of river channel variables such as width, depth, velocity, discharge and efficiency
- Features of changing river channels and valleys
- Ecosystems that exist in a river environment; wetlands and hydroseres - their importance, structure and functioning
- The impact of changing river landforms on people's daily lives - issues of high and low flow, flooding, changing river channels and changing sedimentation levels
- Hazard recurrence level and risk
- A review of management approaches and sustainability
- Human activities in river channel catchments and possible sources of conflict, with particular reference to the following specification options:
    - water quality issues
    - dams and reservoir construction.

Coastal environments

- Key systems which operate within a coastal environment
- Factors which influence the nature of the coastline
- Processes of erosion, transportation and deposition
- Features of coastal environments
- Coastal ecosystems and the impact of human activities
- The impact of change in coastal landforms and processes on human activities - short term and long term
- How human activities have influenced coastal environments - conflicts and consequences with particular reference to recreation and tourism pressures
- A review of management strategies and sustainability.

More detail on what you need to know for each of these elements is given at the beginning of each of the sections.

The hydrological cycle

In this section you will be revising:

- **the hydrological cycle**
- **closed and open systems**

- **drainage basins.**

The hydrological cycle is the movement of moisture and energy between air, land and sea. It varies from place to place and over time. The hydrological cycle is an example of a system in which a set of components is linked.

At the global scale (Figure 1), the hydrological cycle is a **closed system** in which all water is circulated continuously. This process is fuelled by energy from the Sun. There are effectively no gains or losses in the cycle as there is a fixed amount of water.

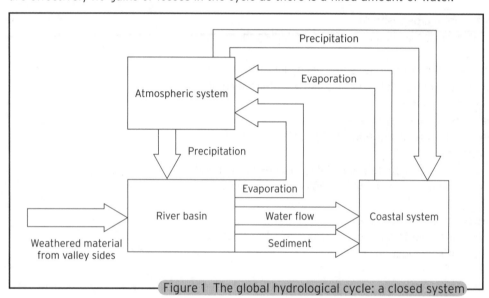

Figure 1 The global hydrological cycle: a closed system

Key concept

An **open system** is a series of inputs, processes and outputs, e.g. a river drainage basin.
A **closed system** is a series of processes, e.g. the *global* hydrological cycle.

A drainage basin is an area of land (a catchment area) drained by a river and its tributaries. Its boundary is marked by a ridge of high land (the watershed), outside of which any precipitation will drain into neighbouring basins.

The river drainage basin is part of the global hydrological cycle and is an **open system**. In a river basin water enters as an input from the atmosphere (precipitation), and leaves the basin as an output either to the ocean (as streamflow or discharge), or to the atmosphere (as evaporation or transpiration), continuing on through the hydrological cycle.

Within a drainage basin there are a series of stores that hold water (Figure 2). These are linked by flows or transfers that allow water to move through the system.

During a storm, the rainfall–runoff processes are likely to change.

Infiltration: water soaking into the soil from the surface

Throughflow: water moving downhill through the soil layers, generally slowly, but flow may concentrate along the line of roots or soil weaknesses which form natural pipes in which the flow will be much faster

Groundwater flow: water moving within rocks below the ground

Precipitation: water deposited on the ground as a liquid or as a solid, for example, rain, hail, snow, fog

Channel flow: water moving downhill within rivers

Overland or surface flow: water moving across the surface of the ground which occurs when rain cannot soak quickly enough into the ground due to tarmac surfaces or hard-baked soil, very heavy rainfall, or when the soil is saturated and infiltration cannot take place (saturated overland flow)

Condensation: the process by which water vapour is converted into water

Depression storage: storage of water in hollows and holes in the ground surface to form puddles

Groundwater store: water held below the water table in aquifers

Percolation: water moving from the surface layers of soil into deeper layers of soil and rock

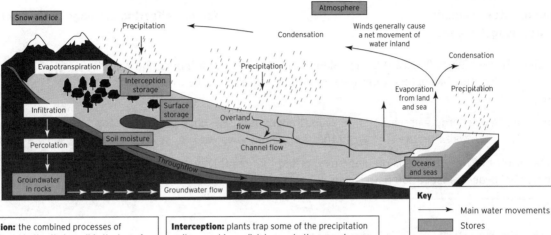

Evapotranspiration: the combined processes of evaporation and transpiration that result in the loss of water from the leaf. Transpiration is the loss of water through the tiny holes called stomata in the leaf surface. In reality, it is very difficult to calculate the two amounts separately, so they are often grouped together

Interception: plants trap some of the precipitation so it may not immediately pass to the ground; some water may drip to the ground as throughfall; some may flow down the stem as stemflow. Alternatively, the precipitation may evaporate directly off the leaf surface and never reach the ground

Evaporation: water changing from its liquid form to a gas (water vapour) and returning to the atmosphere

Figure 2 The hydrological cycle showing main components and movements

Quick check questions

1 Give two examples of how humans might influence the hydrological cycle.

2 Identify two stores and two flows in the drainage basin system.

Reminder

Exam questions may ask you to define one or more of the terms in this section.

Soil moisture budgets

In this section you will be revising:

- **soil moisture budgets**
- **water budget graphs**

- **factors affecting drainage basin discharge.**

The soil moisture budget (Figure 1) is the balance between the water inputs and water outputs. In a drainage basin, this water balance can be represented by the following equation.

Drainage basin discharge = precipitation − evapotranspiration +/− changes in storage, water on the surface, in the soil or groundwater

A visual display of this balance is obtained by plotting the monthly precipitation levels and potential evapotranspiration patterns on a line graph.

Key concept

The wilting point is the limit beyond which plants cannot access the moisture in the soil.

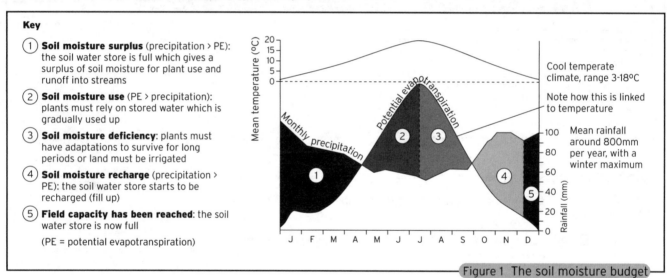

Key

1. **Soil moisture surplus** (precipitation > PE): the soil water store is full which gives a surplus of soil moisture for plant use and runoff into streams
2. **Soil moisture use** (PE > precipitation): plants must rely on stored water which is gradually used up
3. **Soil moisture deficiency**: plants must have adaptations to survive for long periods or land must be irrigated
4. **Soil moisture recharge** (precipitation > PE): the soil water store starts to be recharged (fill up)
5. **Field capacity has been reached**: the soil water store is now full

(PE = potential evapotranspiration)

Cool temperate climate, range 3-18°C

Note how this is linked to temperature

Mean rainfall around 800mm per year, with a winter maximum

Figure 1 The soil moisture budget

By looking at this graph, along with the temperature profile, the hydrological implications of these seasonal changes can be seen.

The water budget also varies between countries and continents, and graphs can be produced for a variety of climatic regions. Figure 2 (page 11) shows a water budget graph for Athens in Greece.

Looking at water budget graphs helps to highlight river-basin management challenges, which include:

- periods when there is likely to be water deficiency or drought
- periods when flooding is most likely to occur
- the best time for irrigation
- longer-term changes in the storage capacity of the drainage basin
- the need for a water transfer system.

However, the water budget variables can be difficult to measure accurately and other factors also affect discharge and water flows within a river-drainage basin, as seen in Figure 3 (page 11).

Reminder

You need to be able to recognise and explain what is happening at different phases of Figure 1.

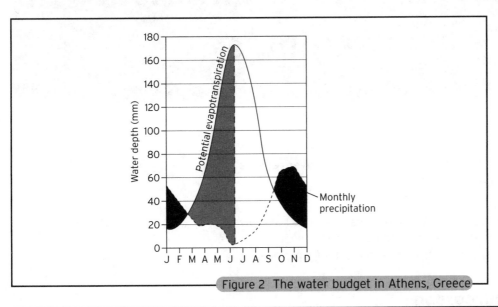

Figure 2 The water budget in Athens, Greece

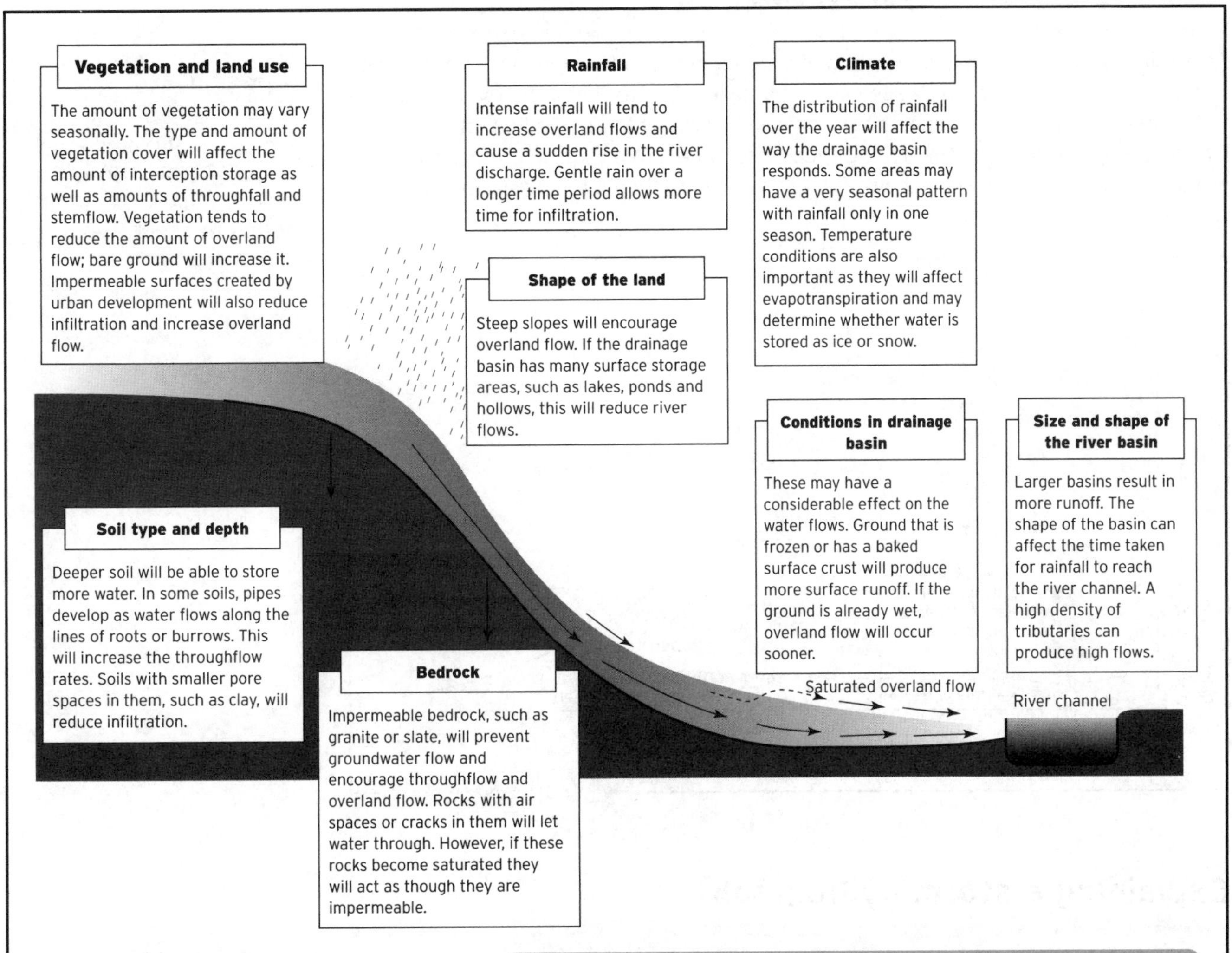

Vegetation and land use

The amount of vegetation may vary seasonally. The type and amount of vegetation cover will affect the amount of interception storage as well as amounts of throughfall and stemflow. Vegetation tends to reduce the amount of overland flow; bare ground will increase it. Impermeable surfaces created by urban development will also reduce infiltration and increase overland flow.

Rainfall

Intense rainfall will tend to increase overland flows and cause a sudden rise in the river discharge. Gentle rain over a longer time period allows more time for infiltration.

Climate

The distribution of rainfall over the year will affect the way the drainage basin responds. Some areas may have a very seasonal pattern with rainfall only in one season. Temperature conditions are also important as they will affect evapotranspiration and may determine whether water is stored as ice or snow.

Shape of the land

Steep slopes will encourage overland flow. If the drainage basin has many surface storage areas, such as lakes, ponds and hollows, this will reduce river flows.

Conditions in drainage basin

These may have a considerable effect on the water flows. Ground that is frozen or has a baked surface crust will produce more surface runoff. If the ground is already wet, overland flow will occur sooner.

Size and shape of the river basin

Larger basins result in more runoff. The shape of the basin can affect the time taken for rainfall to reach the river channel. A high density of tributaries can produce high flows.

Soil type and depth

Deeper soil will be able to store more water. In some soils, pipes develop as water flows along the lines of roots or burrows. This will increase the throughflow rates. Soils with smaller pore spaces in them, such as clay, will reduce infiltration.

Bedrock

Impermeable bedrock, such as granite or slate, will prevent groundwater flow and encourage throughflow and overland flow. Rocks with air spaces or cracks in them will let water through. However, if these rocks become saturated they will act as though they are impermeable.

Saturated overland flow

River channel

Figure 3 Factors that influence water flows within a drainage basin

Quick check questions

QUICK CHECK

1 Explain the water budget graph for Athens, Greece.

2 What implications would there be for water management in the Athens region?

3 How will infiltration rates differ between an area of dense grassland and an urban area?

Hydrographs and river regimes

In this section you will be revising:

- **hydrographs**
- **factors influencing hydrographs**

- **river regimes.**

River discharge is the amount of water in a river passing a given point at a given time. It is measured in cumecs (cubic metres per second). A storm hydrograph is a graph that shows how this river discharge changes as a result of a period of rain.

Reading a storm hydrograph

As it rains, only a very small proportion of the precipitation falls directly into the river channel. Most rain falls on the valley sides and takes time to reach the river. As the water makes its way downslope, the river rises, (shown by the rising limb of the hydrograph), increasing to the point of peak discharge. From that time the amount of water reaching the river as a result of the rainstorm will begin to decrease, and the river level falls.

> **Reminder**
>
> Exam questions asking you to describe and explain **hydrographs** are common, as they test your understanding of many aspects of hydrology (see Figure 1).

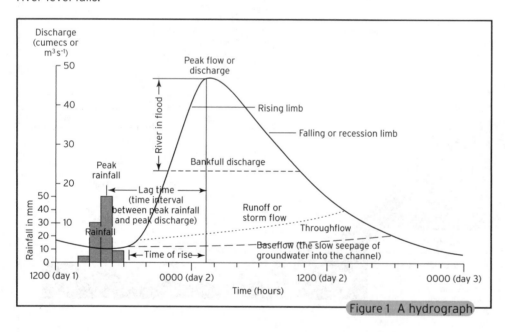

Figure 1 A hydrograph

Explaining a storm hydrograph

The shape of the discharge curve in a hydrograph is related to:

- the quantity and intensity of the rainfall
- the different routes taken by the water to reach the river.

Some examples of hydrographs are shown in Figure 2 (a, b, page 13).

The pattern of seasonal variation in the flow of a river, usually over a period of a year, is known as its regime. A river regime hydrograph shows the river's mean monthly discharge figures and variation results from its response to the region's climate, that is the amount and distribution of rainfall plus the rates of evapotranspiration and snowmelt.

> **Reminder**
>
> **To obtain higher marks** when describing the key features of the hydrograph, make sure that you use specific values from the graph rather than just outlining trends.

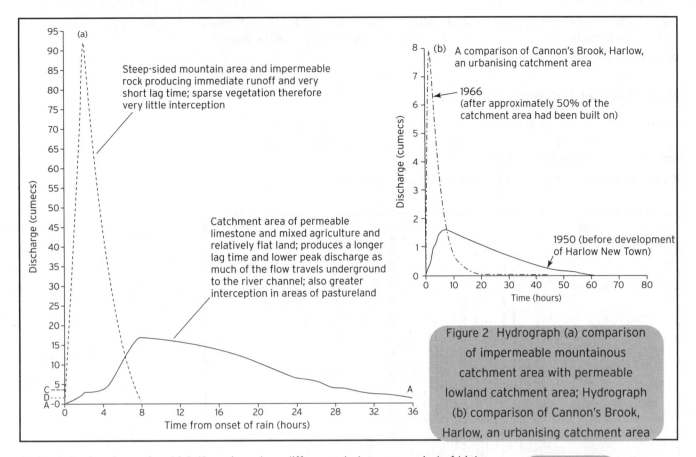

Steep-sided mountain area and impermeable rock producing immediate runoff and very short lag time; sparse vegetation therefore very little interception

Catchment area of permeable limestone and mixed agriculture and relatively flat land; produces a longer lag time and lower peak discharge as much of the flow travels underground to the river channel; also greater interception in areas of pastureland

(b) A comparison of Cannon's Brook, Harlow, an urbanising catchment area

1966
(after approximately 50% of the catchment area had been built on)

1950 (before development of Harlow New Town)

Figure 2 Hydrograph (a) comparison of impermeable mountainous catchment area with permeable lowland catchment area; Hydrograph (b) comparison of Cannon's Brook, Harlow, an urbanising catchment area

A simple regime is one in which there is a clear difference between a period of high water levels and runoff and a period of low water levels and runoff. A complex regime is one in which the pattern of discharge has multiple peaks and/or more variable flow. This often reflects different influences in different parts of the drainage basin.

Large rivers that flow through several distinct regions, and receive water from tributaries in a variety of climatic or relief areas, may have a simple regime in their upper reaches and a complex one towards the river mouth as the effect of the different tributaries is felt in the main channel. The River Rhône is an example of this. The annual flow close to the source, near Geneva in Switzerland, is very different from that near to the mouth, near Beaucaire, in southern France (Figure 3).

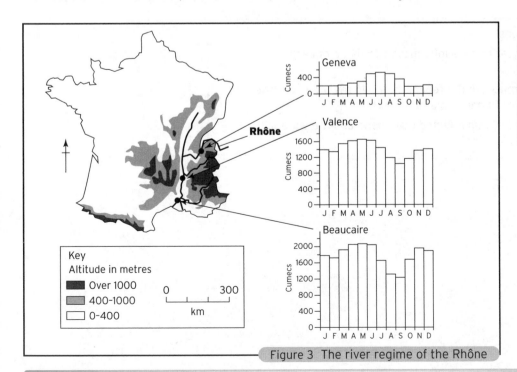

Figure 3 The river regime of the Rhône

The comparison of river regimes before and after human actions on a section of river, such as water abstraction or the construction of a dam, can help to show the impact on river discharge (Figure 4).

Hydrological factors

Physical factors: Size of drainage basin, shape of drainage basin, relief, length of precipitation, intensity of precipitation, type of precipitation, permeability of rock type, and soil texture and structure.

Human influences: Vegetation/deforestation and urbanisation.

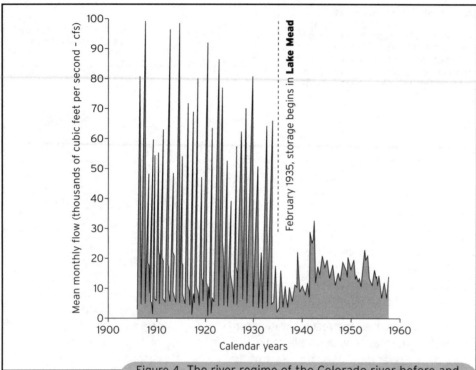

Figure 4 The river regime of the Colorado river before and after the construction of the Hoover Dam

 Quick check questions

1 What factors appear to have influenced the shape of each hydrograph?

2 Explain the differences in the regime between the area near the source of the River Rhône and at its mouth.

3 How has the Hoover Dam affected peak flows and the variability of flow of the Colorado river?

Processes of erosion, transportation and deposition

In this section you will be revising:

- **erosion**
- **transportation**

- **deposition.**

The work of a river involves three main processes: erosion, transportation and deposition.

Erosion

Erosion is the wearing away of the banks and bed of the river. This results in material being picked up and set in motion (entrainment). The eroded material is then transported downstream as load, before **deposition** of the material takes place.

The ability of a river to erode is governed by the amount of energy it possesses. This is determined by:

- potential energy proportional to its volume and height above base level, which is usually sea level
- kinetic energy generated by the movement of water and dependent on river discharge.

A river carries out most erosion and **transportation** when there are high-energy conditions. This is associated with high river flow levels such as following heavy rain or snowmelt.

The velocity of a river is influenced by three main factors:

1 channel shape in cross-section
2 roughness of the channel's bed and banks
3 channel slope.

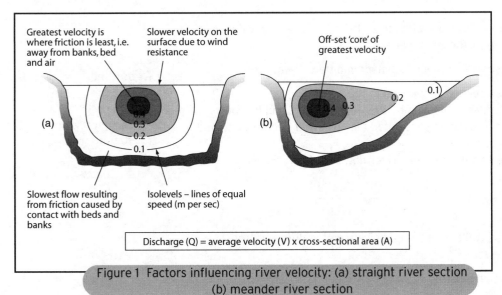

Greatest velocity is where friction is least, i.e. away from banks, bed and air

Slower velocity on the surface due to wind resistance

Off-set 'core' of greatest velocity

(a)

(b)

0.4 0.3 0.2 0.1

0.3
0.2
0.1

Slowest flow resulting from friction caused by contact with beds and banks

Isolevels – lines of equal speed (m per sec)

Discharge (Q) = average velocity (V) x cross-sectional area (A)

Figure 1 Factors influencing river velocity: (a) straight river section (b) meander river section

Reminder

Look at how some of the energy of a river is lost by friction with the bed and banks or through turbulence.

Potentially, higher rates of erosion correspond with:

- heavier and sharper loads
- higher river velocity
- increased gradient
- soft, unconsolidated material such as sand and gravel
- low pH (acidic); increased rates of solution
- higher levels of certain types of human impact such as deforestation or river channel alterations that interfere with the natural flow of the river.

A river is most efficient at bankfull.

Processes of erosion

A river may erode by any of four processes (Figure 2).

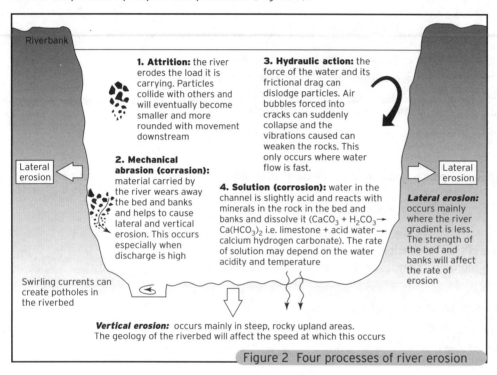

Figure 2 Four processes of river erosion

A particle protruding from the river is also subject to a lift force caused by water accelerating over it. This is known as the Bernoulli effect.

Transportation A river can transport its eroded sediment in different ways too:

- **Suspension:** tiny particles can remain suspended in the water
- **Solution:** products of solution can be carried by the water even during low flows
- **Saltation:** particles too large to become suspended may be lifted and dropped and gradually move downstream as a result
- **Traction:** larger particles (bedload) slide when river flows are fast; smaller stones may assist this movement.

> **Reminder**
>
> **Deposition** occurs when the river no longer has enough energy to transport the load it is carrying.

Quick check questions

1 Why is the velocity profile on a straight river section different from that in a meander section?

2 Why is a river channel most efficient at bankfull?

3 Are the types of transportation likely to be different in the upper reaches of a river to near the river mouth? (Think about the size of particles you find at the source compared with those at the mouth.)

In this section you will be revising:

- river velocity
- river profiles
- river cross-sections.

River velocity

The velocity of a river is influenced by gravity and friction. Gravity causes the river to move downslope, so velocity increases as slopes steepen. As water moves downstream, the river will seek the path of least resistance; that is one that will maximise velocity and minimise the loss of energy caused by friction. Most friction occurs along the banks and bed of the river, but there is also friction in the water mass.

River profiles

Many rivers follow a **long profile**, which is smooth and concave in shape (Figure 1). This is known as a graded profile.

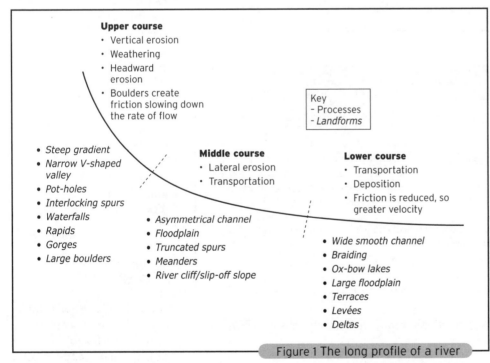

Upper course
- Vertical erosion
- Weathering
- Headward erosion
- Boulders create friction slowing down the rate of flow

Key
- Processes
- *Landforms*

- *Steep gradient*
- *Narrow V-shaped valley*
- *Pot-holes*
- *Interlocking spurs*
- *Waterfalls*
- *Rapids*
- *Gorges*
- *Large boulders*

Middle course
- Lateral erosion
- Transportation

- *Asymmetrical channel*
- *Floodplain*
- *Truncated spurs*
- *Meanders*
- *River cliff/slip-off slope*

Lower course
- Transportation
- Deposition
- Friction is reduced, so greater velocity

- *Wide smooth channel*
- *Braiding*
- *Ox-bow lakes*
- *Large floodplain*
- *Terraces*
- *Levées*
- *Deltas*

Figure 1 The long profile of a river

This type of profile is the model shape that all rivers try to reach as they adjust their course to **base level**. Bradshaw summarised the main trends in the long profile of a river (see Figure 2 on page 18).

River cross-sections

Cross-sectional area increases downstream and the channel becomes larger and more efficient. The extra water comes from tributaries joining the main channel. Increased efficiency results from changing the wetted perimeter and hydraulic radius.

Reminder

Velocity increases with distance downriver as:
- the river is more efficient
- the hydraulic radius is higher, i.e. there is proportionally less contact between the water and the river bed and banks, which means less 'drag' effect
- the roughness of the river bed and bank has decreased; therefore there is less friction to slow the water down
- the lower channel gradient is counteracted by the lower friction.

Key concepts

The **long profile** is shown by plotting a line graph of a river's height above base level against distance from its source.
Base level is the theoretical limit, usually sea level, below which rivers cannot erode their courses.
The **wetted perimeter** is the surface of the river's bed and banks which is in contact with the water in the channel.

Manning devised a formula to explain the link between river variables, where Q is discharge, A is cross-sectional area, R is hydraulic radius, S is gradient, n is Manning's coefficient of bed roughness.

$$Q = A \times \frac{R^{0.67} \times S^{0.5}}{n}$$

Examples of Manning's coefficient of bed roughness are shown in Table 1.

As a river moves downstream, the particles of the river load decrease in size and increase in roundness. This means that they are more mobile than the larger, more angular particles upstream, which therefore helps to increase downstream velocities. These particles also help to smooth the bed and banks of the channel, further increasing velocities.

Discharge is also affected by:

- the characteristics of tributaries and the location of the point at which a tributary meets the main river
- rock type and structure: surface runoff is greater in areas of impermeable rock; it reaches the channel much faster than underground flow in permeable rock
- land use: discharge is higher in scarcely vegetated, urbanised and deforested areas as there is greater surface runoff
- human influences: humans may add water to a river, for example at a sewage outfall, or they can remove water, for example abstraction of drinking water.

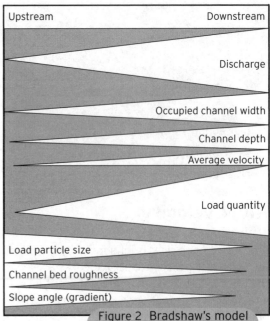

Figure 2 Bradshaw's model of the long profile of a river

Type of river channel	Manning's coefficient of bed roughness
Concrete drainage channel	0.013
Alluvial channels with small ripples	0.014 – 0.024
Winding natural channel	0.025
Mountain stream with rocky beds	0.04 – 0.05

Table 1

Key concept

The **hydraulic radius** is the ratio between the area of the cross-section of the river channel and the length of the wetted perimeter. The higher the number the greater the efficiency.

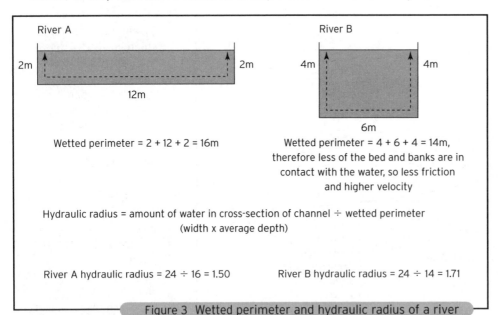

Figure 3 Wetted perimeter and hydraulic radius of a river

Rejuvenation

Sometimes the long profile shows irregularities in this smooth profile. If base level is changed the river will try to adjust accordingly. If it falls, as during tectonic uplift of the land, then a process called rejuvenation occurs (Figure 4, page 19). With this, there is an increase in gradient and therefore in velocity of the river and its erosive power. The new base level starts at the sea and gradually erodes back up the river. The point of change is marked by the knickpoint, and often a resultant waterfall. If base level rises, as during an interglacial period, adjustment focuses on deposition rather than erosion.

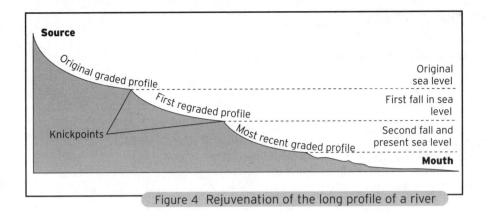

Figure 4 Rejuvenation of the long profile of a river

Afon Glaslyn, North Wales

The cross-section below shows the long profile of the *Afon* (river) *Glaslyn* (see Figure 5) in North Wales. It is a useful example as it shows changes downstream in the river profile, processes, material size and landforms.

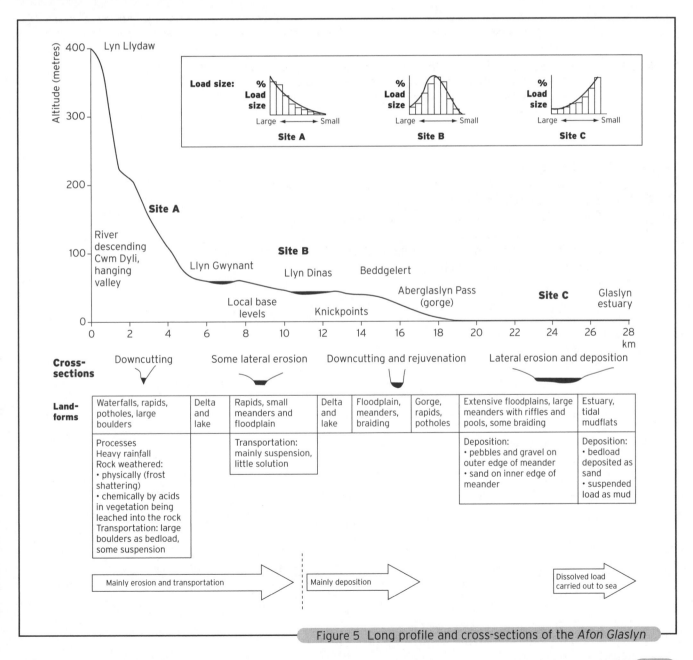

Figure 5 Long profile and cross-sections of the *Afon Glaslyn*

Fieldwork techniques in river study

Fieldwork techniques used to study the characteristics of a river section are shown in Table 2.

Characteristics of a river	Fieldwork method
Width and depth	Stretch a tape measure across a section of river to measure the width. Use a metre rule to measure the river depth at intervals across the same section. Plotting these measurements on graph paper reproduces the channel cross-section. Multiplying width by average depth gives the cross-sectional area of the channel.
Velocity (ms⁻¹)	Select and measure a known distance, usually 5 or 10 metres. Record the time taken for a float (a coloured ball) to pass over the distance. Because rivers vary in their speed, three velocity readings are usually taken – at the left bank, the right bank and as close as possible to the centre of the channel. River velocity is found by dividing the distance by the time taken in seconds.
Discharge (cumecs)	Discharge is the amount of water that passes a point in a given time. This is calculated by multiplying the cross-sectional area by the average velocity.
Sediment size and shape	Size can be measured in different ways, but is usually measured by taking the longest axis. One way to assess roundness of the particles on a visual scale is to compare them to an accepted scale (e.g. Powers, which has six classes) from very angular through to well rounded.

Table 2

Reminder

If you have carried out river fieldwork at a particular location as part of your course, think about what data you collected and how. This could be used as a good specific example.

Quick check questions
1 Describe the downstream changes in the different indicators in Figure 2.
2 Explain why discharge increases downstream.
3 Suggest reasons for the downstream increase in load quantity but the decrease in load particle size.
4 Using the long profile of the Afon Glaslyn (Figure 5), explain the changes in landforms along the profile.

1.6 Features of changing river channels and valleys

In this section you will be revising:

- **upper course features of erosion**
- **middle course features of erosion and deposition**
- **lower course features of deposition.**

Rivers are important in shaping the landscape. They erode, transport and deposit material that produces a variety of landforms. There is a close relationship between velocity, discharge and channel characteristics.

Upper course: features of erosion

Waterfalls

- Waterfalls frequently occur on horizontally-bedded rocks (Figure 1).
- The soft overlying rock is undercut by hydraulic action and abrasion.
- The weight of the water and the lack of support cause the overhanging rock to collapse.
- After collapse, some of the rock will be swirled around by the river, especially during times of high discharge, to form a deep plunge pool.
- Over thousands of years this process is repeated many times causing the waterfall to produce headward retreat, (i.e. up the river).
- This may form a gorge of recession, such as at Niagara Falls which is retreating by one metre per year.
- Rapids occur where the layers of hard and soft rock are very thin and so no obvious break of slope develops as a waterfall.

Key concepts

Vertical erosion is characteristic of fast-flowing rivers that are transporting a large bedload of coarse, hard particles. The particles abraid and pothole the riverbed but the resistant rocks of the valley slopes restrict weathering of the slopes either side.
Headward erosion occurs either at the source of the river, where the length of the channel is increased, or at points where the long profile of the river is locally steep, for example, the gradual retreat of a waterfall.

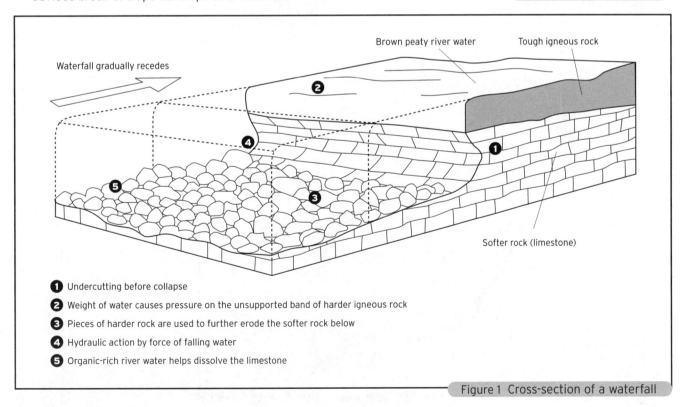

Brown peaty river water   Tough igneous rock

Waterfall gradually recedes

❷

❹

❺   ❸   ❶

Softer rock (limestone)

❶ Undercutting before collapse

❷ Weight of water causes pressure on the unsupported band of harder igneous rock

❸ Pieces of harder rock are used to further erode the softer rock below

❹ Hydraulic action by force of falling water

❺ Organic-rich river water helps dissolve the limestone

Figure 1 Cross-section of a waterfall

V-shaped valleys and interlocking spurs

- Any spare energy possessed by the river near its source will be used to transport large boulders along its bed. This results in the river cutting rapidly downwards.
- This vertical erosion produces steep-sided, narrow valleys shaped like the letter 'V'.
- The valley sides are steep due to soil and loose rock being washed downhill, following periods of heavy rainfall, and added to the load of the river.
- The river is forced to wind its way around protruding hillsides of more resistant rock which are known as interlocking spurs.

Potholes

These are formed by swirling water using boulders and stones to erode a small depression in the riverbed (see Figure 2).

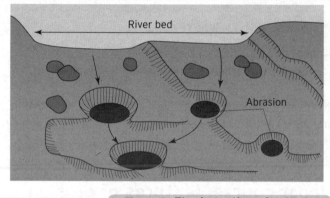

Figure 2 The formation of potholes

Middle course: features of erosion and deposition

Pools and riffles

These are formed by turbulence. Eddies cause the deposition of coarse sediment (riffles) at high velocity points and fine sediments (pools) at low velocity areas. Riffles have a steeper gradient than pools, which leads to sinuosity. Riffles occur at an interval of approximately six times the channel width.

Meanders

Meanders are characterised by bends in the river (Figure 3). The wavelength of meanders is dependent on channel width, discharge and the nature of the bed and banks.

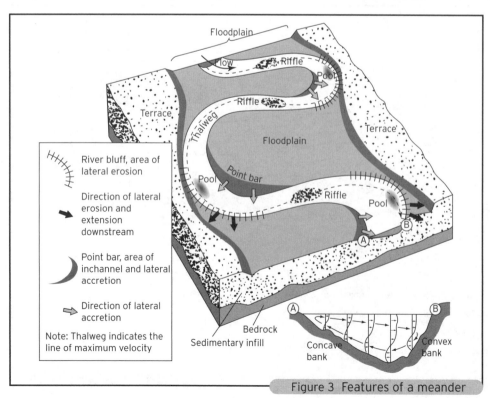

Figure 3 Features of a meander

There is no single explanation of the cause of meandering, but a number of factors have been suggested (see Figure 4).

- Friction with the channel bed and bank cause turbulence which makes the stream flow unstable. This produces helicoidal flow (a corkscrew water motion) and sandbars along the channel.
- Sinuosity develops on moderate angles. At low gradients, helicoidal flow is insufficient to produce alternating pools and riffles. High velocity flows on steep gradients are too strong and braided channels are formed.
- Helicoidal flow causes the line of fastest flow (the thalweg) to move from side to side within the channel. This increases the amplitude of the meander.

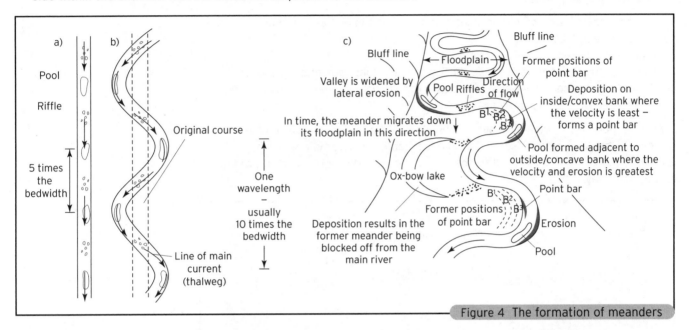

Figure 4 The formation of meanders

Meanders can also change over time. They:

- migrate downstream and erode river cliffs
- migrate laterally (sideways) which results in a greatly widened floodplain
- become exaggerated and can be cut off to form ox-bow lakes
- become intrenched or ingrown, under special circumstances.

Braiding

Braiding occurs when a river splits into many channels separated by banks of sediment (Figure 5). These deposits (also called chars or eyots) may rapidly and frequently change their position. Braiding tends to occur when:

- the river has a large bed load
- the discharge is variable, and therefore its capacity to carry sediment varies, for example, due to seasonal rainfall or snowmelt
- the banks are made of material that easily erodes
- a river level falls rapidly, reducing its competence and capacity, and choking the channel with material.

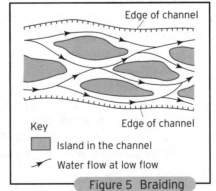

Key
- Island in the channel
- Water flow at low flow

Figure 5 Braiding

The change from one form of channel shape to another, (meandering to braiding), can occur due to an external change in energy, such as the construction of a reservoir, or a slow natural internal change such as the readjustment after a storm event.

Lower course: features of deposition

Reminder

See Section 1.8, page 29, for more detail on capacity and competence of a river.

Deposition occurs when the capacity and competence of a river reduces or when the load suddenly increases, perhaps due to a landslide into the river.

Floodplain

Rivers have most energy when at bankfull stage. Should the river continues to rise, water will flood onto adjacent flat land carrying with it suspended sediment. This causes:

- a sudden increase in wetted perimeter and decrease in hydraulic radius
- an increase in friction
- a decrease in velocity
- the deposition of material (alluvium). The coarsest load (gravel and sand) is deposited as raised banks or levées closer to the channel; finer sediment, (clay and silt) is carried further away.

With each flood a thin veneer of silt is deposited on the floodplain, which causes it to increase in height. Some sediment is also deposited in the river channel, which increases the risk of flooding still further. If water bursts through a levée it produces a crevasse splay.

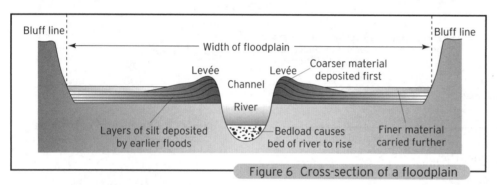

Figure 6 Cross-section of a floodplain

Terraces

A terrace is a flat strip of land along the valley side, parallel to the floodplain and separated from it by a steep slope. The oldest terraces are the highest. Terraces are formed when
- the downcutting of a river occurs faster than the lateral migration of meanders
- a river passes from resistant beds (eroded slower) to less resistant beds (eroded faster)
- meanders migrate and therefore erode the floodplain
- there is a drop in sea level or a rise in the height of the land
- human activity, such as deforestation, reduces vegetation cover which may result in increased runoff and the accelerated erosion of part of the floodplain.

Deltas

Deltas are flat areas of land at the mouth of a river extending out into the sea. Deltas are crossed by many streams, called distributaries. These are often flanked by levées which are joined together by spits and bars sealing off shallow areas of water to form lagoons. The lagoons are gradually infilled by silt and sand to form marshes and eventually colonised by vegetation.

Deltas are formed by river deposition under special conditions.
- The river must be carrying a large load. The Mississippi River, for example, carries about 450 million tonnes of sediment into the delta distributaries every year.
- The material must be deposited faster than its removal by the action of the tides, waves and currents.

- Most deltas occur in calm seas with a gently sloping seabed. These seas usually have very small tides or no tides at all.
- As the river meets the sea its velocity is slowed and deposition occurs.
- The river floods frequently in its lower course, depositing alluvium in the delta, building up levées and creating new distributaries.

The Ganges delta is one of the largest deltas in the world. It is formed at the confluence of three huge rivers: the Ganges, Jamuna (Brahmaputra) and Meghna. Together these rivers drain an area of over two million square kilometres, including parts of India and Nepal as well as the whole of Bangladesh. Bangladesh is very low-lying; few areas exceed ten metres above sea level, which puts it under constant threat from flooding and rising sea levels. The country is also densely populated (>900 people per sq km), with rapid population growth, (2.7% per year).

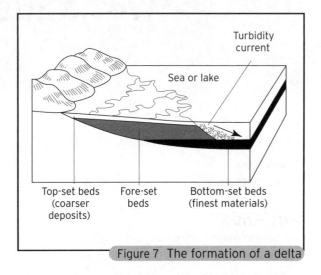

Figure 7 The formation of a delta

Alluvial fans

Alluvial fans are fan-shaped landforms similar to deltas but deposited on land. They often occur:

- where a stream comes from a steep mountain course and enters a flatter plain with a low gradient, for example, at Spitzbergen in Norway
- in glacial, temperate or semi-arid environments where there are rapidly changing stream discharges, for example, in the glaciated valley of the River Rhône in Switzerland. Here streams have highly variable discharges between winter and summer and are often braided.

Estuaries

When a river reaches the sea its velocity and therefore its competence to transport sediment, is reduced. This may produce a delta (Figure 7).

An estuary is the part of a river mouth within which tides have an effect and therefore where fresh and saline water are mixed. The deposition of clay in deltas is helped by *flocculation*. In fresh water, charged clay particles repel each other but salt water changes this and they form clots which settle more quickly.

Most present-day estuaries were formed when a coastal area subsided or there was a rise in sea level, causing the lower part of the river to be drowned. Estuaries are sheltered so they often contain much deposited sediment due to reduced velocity. Deposition will continue if the river supplies more sediment than can be removed by tidal streams and by what little wave action is possible within the estuary. The incoming and outgoing tidal streams often erode an intricate shifting pattern of channels in the sediments. The Wash is the largest British estuary, occupying 66,600 hectares.

Quick check questions

1 What processes of erosion are likely to be occurring to create potholes?

2 Describe how a meander migrates downstream.

3 How might humans influence the natural processes on a floodplain?

4 Why do deltas not continue to develop beyond a certain distance into the sea?

Wetlands and hydroseres

In this section you will be revising:

- **wetlands**
- **ecosystems**

- **hydroseres.**

Wetlands

Wetlands have many important functions.

- Sedimentation: wetlands trap water, allowing the deposition of nutrient-rich sediment for agriculture such as rice farming.
- Pollution control: wetlands are known as the 'kidneys' of the rivers/sea. Wetland plants (reeds) and bacteria trap and break down sewage and farm runoff. Metals from factory discharges fall to the bottom of the silt beds where they are 'locked' away limiting the harm they can do.
- Flood protection: peatlands can store water quickly but release it slowly, while, as their height increases, saltmarshes can protect coastlines.
- Wildlife sanctuaries: many birds breed on wetlands, or during migration, use them as sources of food.
- As a source of fuel and building materials: peat provides a source of fuel while reeds and mangroves are used as building materials.

Wetlands are facing a variety of threats, including:

- the destruction of habitats and consequently of related plants and animal species, especially from urban and agricultural development
- drainage
- increased water abstraction from ground and surface waters
- pollution, nutrient enrichment and siltation
- modification or loss of physical features, for example, river channelisation
- introduction of non-native species
- intensive fisheries management
- inappropriate development of recreation and navigation.

> ### Reminder
>
> In 1971, the Ramsar Convention was signed by 92 countries because of increasing concern over the rate of loss of wetlands. So far, 776 sites have been placed on the Ramsar List.

Ecosystems

An **ecosystem** is a community of plants and animals living together with the environment in which they live. It has two elements:

- abiotic (non-living) such as rocks, soil, water
- biotic (living) such as plants, animals and micro-organisms.

Together these elements are arranged in a structure:

- layers of vegetation
- food web – the relationship between different species
- biomass, the amount of living matter
- dead organic matter (DOM) made up of dead and decaying matter.

An ecosystem functions in two ways, which are closely linked:

- energy flow shown by trophic (or feeding) levels (Figure 1)
- the cycling of nutrients (see also *Changing Environments*, pages 50-51).

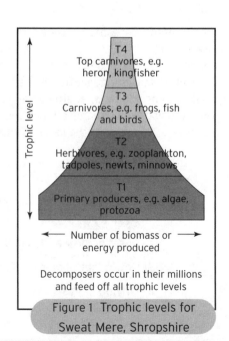

Figure 1 Trophic levels for Sweat Mere, Shropshire

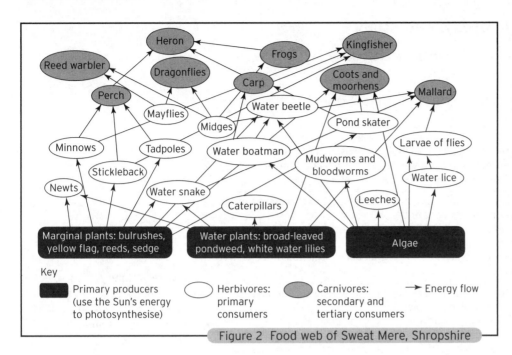

Key

| Primary producers (use the Sun's energy to photosynthesise) | Herbivores: primary consumers | Carnivores: secondary and tertiary consumers | → Energy flow |

Figure 2 Food web of Sweat Mere, Shropshire

Reminder

Sweat Mere in Shropshire is used as an example of a hydrosere throughout this section and on pages 47-51, *Changing Environments*, Heinemann 2000.
The **Florida Everglades** provide another case study of an ecosystem under threat from intensive land use and tourism. See pages 54-57, *Changing Environments*, Heinemann 2000.

Nutrients are chemical elements and compounds needed by plants for growth. Energy flows through ecosystems and is eventually lost, but nutrients are cycled within the ecosystem, between the main nutrient pools of the atmosphere, lithosphere and hydrosphere.

One example of an ecosystem is a hydrosere, that is, the plant succession (or stages of change) that occurs in shallow fresh water such as in a pond or at the margins of a lake (Figure 3).

Hydrosere stage							
1	2	3	4	5	6	7	8
Open water; algae, water lilies	Bulrushes	Sedges	Willow, alder	Alder	Alder, birch	Birch	Oak

Plants and habitat							
Habitat description	Reed swamp	Marsh or fen	Open wooded fen	Closed wooded fen	Woodland		
Habitat processes	Accelerated deposition of silt and clay; floating raft of organic matter forms and thickens		Raft now a mat resting on mineral soil	Black mineral soil revealed in patches; earthworms	Ground level now above water table; oak seedlings	Birch canopy forms; oak saplings	Oak grows through and then over the birch
pH level	–	–	7.3		4.3	3.7	–
Number of species of plant	6	10	14	26	18	14	10

Figure 3 Hydrosere at Sweat Mere, Shropshire

Fieldwork techniques in ecosystem study

Examples of field surveys to assess ecosystem structure, quality and diversity are shown in Table 1.

Survey focus	Field technique
Physical conditions	Record moisture levels, pH and light levels using hand-held meters. Soil samples taken for laboratory analysis or by using a soil auger at regular points along a transect from pond side to further inland (to the area of woodland if possible) – soil type, texture, pH, moisture.
Vegetation structure and diversity	Quadrat survey at regular intervals along the transect to represent typical vegetation of the different stages of the hydrosere. Recorded results likely to include: percentage coverage of vegetation, number and variety of species, vegetation height. From this data, association can be considered and calculation of a diversity index such as Simpson's.
Organisms	Fall and/or catch traps used to collect and identify pond-side organisms; a beating tray used to collect samples from shrubs. A tow net dragged along the surface layers of the pond and a kick sample from the bottom sediment will obtain organisms in the water itself. Observation and identification of footprints, droppings and or habitats, (e.g. rabbit holes) for larger animals.

Table 1

Quick check questions

1 What could be done to minimise the main threats to wetland areas?

2 How does a food chain differ from a food web?

3 Why are there usually only four or five levels in a trophic pyramid?

4 Outline the different stages in a hydrosere.

5 How might human influence affect a hydrosere?

River channel load and sediment budgets

In this section you will be revising:

- **river load**
- **weathering**

- **sediment yields**
- **Hjulstrom Curves.**

River load

If the velocity of the river is high, the amount of energy still available after overcoming the friction caused by riverbed materials will be high, and so turbulence increases. This results in riverbed sediment being disturbed and carried downriver. The faster the river flow, the larger the quantity and size of particles which will be transported. The transported material is known as river load.

When the velocity is low, there is less energy to overcome friction. Turbulence is very low which means that some sediment may be deposited.

A river's load is divided into three main types:

1 solution load: dissolved minerals carried as chemical ions
2 suspended load: particles of clay and silt held up by the turbulent flow
3 bed load: larger particles moved by saltation, rolling and sliding, usually under conditions of high energy.

Weathering

Material can also enter the river channel from elsewhere in the river valley by weathering and mass movement (see Figure 1).

Key concept

Weathering is the disintegration of rocks at a particular location. **Mass movement** also involves the movement of that material, for example down the valley side.

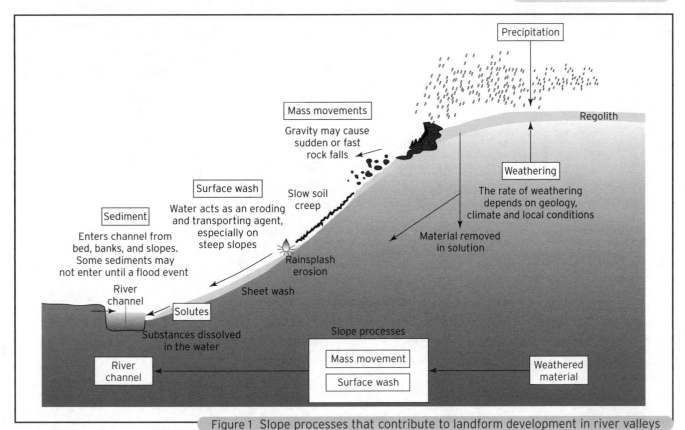

Figure 1 Slope processes that contribute to landform development in river valleys

Weathering can fall into three broad categories.

1   Mechanical or physical: weathering without any significant change in the chemical or mineral composition of the rock, for example, freeze thaw.
2   Chemical: the decomposition of rocks by the action of air, water or acid, for example, oxidation or carbonation.
3   Biological: the breakdown of rocks and minerals by the activities of plants, animals and micro-organisms, for example, by bacteria or plant roots.

In practice, the overall weathering process may be involve an interaction of these three types.

Sediment yields

Sediment yields vary considerably worldwide. For example, the Huang He in China has a yield of 900 10^8 tyr^{-1}, due to a large zone of unconsolidated material in the catchment area, yet the River Nile only yields 2 10^8 tyr^{-1}.

Human activity can have a considerable effect on sediment yields:

Increased sediment

- Mining
- Early construction phases of urbanisation
- Deforestation
- Bare arable ground.

Decreased sediment
(i.e. sediment stores are created)

- Contour ploughing and terracing
- Dams and reservoirs
- Irrigation
- Fallow land / permanent pasture.

The Hjulstrom Curve

The load of a river basin varies with discharge and velocity. The relationships between these variables is shown by the Hjulstrom Curve (Figure 2). **Mean flow** is used to define conditions of sediment entrainment, transport and deposition. Hjulstrom Curves shown the **competence** at any given velocity.

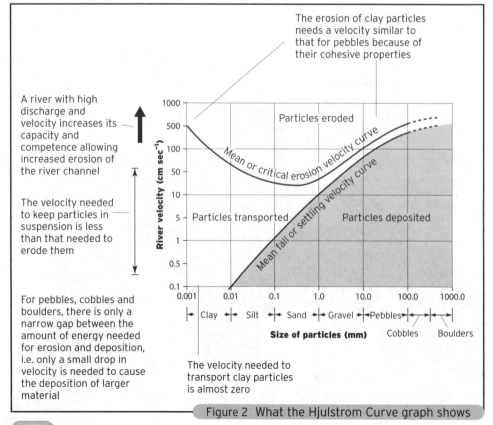

Figure 2 What the Hjulstrom Curve graph shows

Some issues with using the Hjulstrom Curve:

- Mean annual flow is used rather than velocity at the channel bed where the sediment is actually located.
- Water velocity increases with depth.
- The Hjulstrom Curve refers to smooth channels, whereas most natural channels are irregular.
- Flow in a naturally flowing river is variable, whereas curves suggest a regular flow.

QUICK CHECK — Quick check questions

1 How would the climate of a region effect the relative proportion of each of the types of weathering occurring in that region?

2 Identify ways in which humans could influence the weathering process.

3 Describe and explain what the Hjulstrom Curve shows.

Key concepts

Capacity is the largest amount of debris that a stream can carry.
Competence is the diameter of the largest particle that can be carried.
Critical erosion velocity is the lowest velocity at which grains of a given size can be eroded.
Fall or **settling velocity** is the mean velocity at which grains are too large or heavy to continue to be transported for the velocity of the river at a particular time. This reflects the size, density and shape of the particle as well as the velocity and density of the transporting water.

Flooding and the impact of rivers on human activities

In this section you will be revising:

- **causes of flooding**
- **risk and recurrence levels of flooding**
- **case study of flooding**

- **low flow issues**
- **impact of rivers on human activities.**

Causes of flooding

Physical	Human
Climatological: - intense precipitation (rainfall intensity > infiltration capacity) common in semi-arid areas - prolonged period of rainfall produces saturation of the soil and overland flow - a sudden increase in temperature producing rapid snowmelt, which can be made worse by frozen ground limiting infiltration Nature of the basin: - infiltration rate depends on rock and soil type - shape of the river basin, relief/gradient and vegetation cover affects how quickly runoff reaches the channel Coastal influences: - high seasonal tides, storm surges, tropical cyclones can result in higher water levels in rivers and low-lying coastal areas, (e.g. in Bangladesh)	Deforestation reduces interception and evapotranspiration, and therefore increases runoff; possible decrease in channel capacity, due to increased amount of sediment being carried into the river channel, such as in the Maracá rainforest in the Amazon Basin Urbanisation increases the magnitude and frequency of floods by: - the creation of highly impermeable surfaces such as roads, roofs and pavements - smooth surfaces served by a dense network of drains, gutters and underground sewers, effectively increasing drainage density - natural river channels are often constricted by bridge supports or riverside facilities, reducing their carrying capacity - straightening river channels and lining them with concrete as part of building projects lead to faster delivery of water downstream Failure of hard engineering, such as a dam burst, can produce catastrophic flooding, for example, dam burst in an iron ore mine near Seville, Spain in 1999 Land management techniques such as drainage systems, digging ditches or ploughing up and down a slope will decrease lagtime for the water to reach the river channel

Table 1 Causes of flooding

Recurrence level and risk

Flooding occurs when the capacity of a river is exceeded and water overtops the riverbanks and flows onto the surrounding land. A natural event becomes a hazard when it affects human activities in areas such as river valleys or low-lying coastal areas.

Risk is affected by:

- the frequency of flooding; how often floods can be expected
- the magnitude of the flood; how severe or large each occurrence will be
- the number and density of people living in the affected area
- the amount of flood protection and efficiency of prediction systems
- the level of economic development; this affects an area's ability to afford management strategies and preparedness, and its ability to cope in an emergency, (for example, evacuation procedures, rescue and emergency facilities).

Key concept

Risk assessment is the process of finding the probability (how likely it is to happen) that a hazardous event of a particular size will occur within a given period of time and estimating its impact.

Benefits of flooding:

- replenishes groundwater reserves
- provides nutrient-rich sediment for agriculture in the dry season
- reduces the need for artificial fertilisers
- flushes pollutants and pathogens away from domestic areas
- may increase the fish supply.

Key concept

Recurrence level is the interval at which a particular level of flooding is likely to occur.

Case study: Flooding in Bangladesh, 1998

Reminder

For more details on other case studies, see pages 28-45 in *Changing Environments*, Heinemann 2000.

Physical causes	Human causes
• 80 per cent of the country is floodplain and delta (less than one metre above sea level) due to the confluence of three rivers – the Ganges, Jamuna and Meghna • Tropical cyclones bring heavy rain and storm surges cause coastal floods • Snowmelt from the Himalayas in late spring and summer increases discharge • Heavy monsoon rains, especially over the Himalayas, the uplands in Assam and the Central Indian Plateau are the main cause of flooding • The Himalayas are still growing with earthquakes that results in erosion and increased loads of sediments for rivers to carry which increases the flood risk	• Deforestation; rapidly-increasing populations in Nepal and Tibet have resulted in the removal of large areas of forest to provide grazing land, fuel and building material. This has reduced interception and increased overland flow, soil erosion and landslides which increases the river bed and the flood risk • Dam building: during the dry season the Farraka Dam, built in 1971 in India, reduces the downstream discharge and encourages sedimentation • Global warming may possibly be producing higher rainfall in Nepal and a rise in sea level • Urbanisation, including the construction of more roads and impermeable concrete surfaces, speeds runoff to the main channel, while embankments slow drainage of flood waters from the land

Table 2 Causes of flooding in Bangladesh, 1998

Impact of flooding in 1998

- 57 per cent of the land area was flooded.
- Over 1000 people were killed and millions made homeless.
- Large areas of farmland and many properties were washed away.
- There were severe shortages of drinking water and food.
- There were enormous health and hygiene problems; many people were affected by diarrhoea or respiratory problems.
- An embankment protecting Sandwip, a large coastal island, was breached marooning 1200 families.
- In the Nalbari district, 240 villages were submerged.
- A major clear up operation was needed afterwards to remove rotting crops and wrecked roads and buildings.
- Overall, the floods cost $1 billion.

Low flow issues

These are likely to be caused by:

- drought conditions
- dam construction which regulates downstream river discharge and the regime of the river, affects the migratory routes of some fish, and leads to an increase in salts and pollutants. For example, in the Russian Federation, dams have reduced natural discharge from the Dnestr, Dnepr and Don rivers by 50–60 per cent and have caused an accumulation of salts and pollution in the Black Sea coastal waters

○ over abstraction which can lead to water shortages, deteriorating water quality, increased sedimentation and ecological changes. For example, in the River Colorado basin area, USA, there has been a growing demand for water due to
- the aridity of many areas within the catchment
- extraction of water to irrigate agricultural areas in the central valley of California
- expansion of urban areas and the demand for water supplies such as in the 'Sansan' megalopolis area.

As a result

○ there is very little flow by the time the river reaches the Gulf of Mexico
○ there is an increase in salinity (up to 3000ppm) due to water loss through evaporation during the irrigation process. Mexico has been forced to spend $200m on a desalinisation plant in order to be able to use the remaining water
○ water quotas have been introduced for the use of water from the river; California currently uses around 59 per cent of the water.

Other impacts of rivers on human activities

Changing river channels

Migration of the river channel layout, especially in meander sections, can influence:

○ places of erosion or possible river cliff collapse
○ land ownership if the river acts as the boundary.

For example, look at the diagram below of the Kentucky Bar, Mayersville Reach on the Mississippi River (see Figure 1).

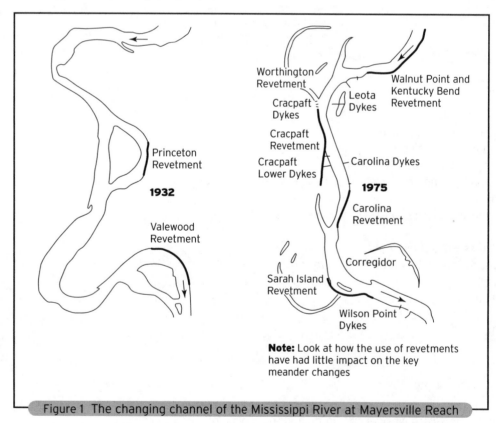

Figure 1 The changing channel of the Mississippi River at Mayersville Reach

Changing sedimentation levels

Positive effects:

- alluvium deposited from rivers is rich in nutrients and can benefit riverside farmers.

Negative effects of too much sediment can cause problems such as:

- limiting the channel capacity and increasing the risk of flooding
- blocking irrigation channels
- infilling lakes and reservoirs, therefore decreasing their efficiency
- blocking shipping channels unless they are dredged regularly
- reducing the sunlight in ponds which may make conditions unsuitable for stream life adapted to clear water.

Contaminated sediments may affect the quality of water supplies and/or discolour the water.

The Farakka Dam in India was built to divert millions of tonnes of water from the River Ganges into the River Hooghly for water supplies and to flush out the build up of sediment in the port of Calcutta.

Factors that affect the sediment input into a river channel

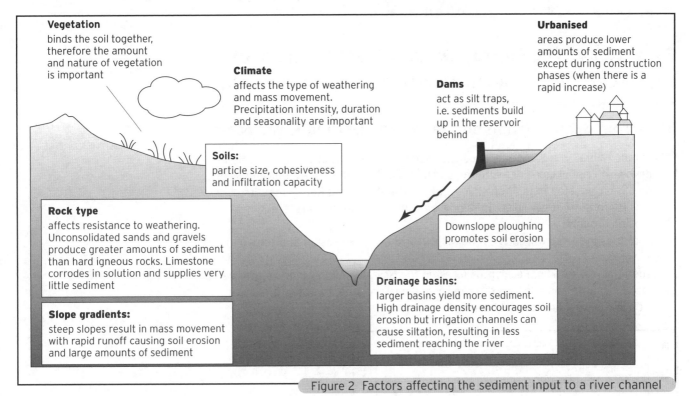

Figure 2 Factors affecting the sediment input to a river channel

Quick check questions
1 Explain why the number of deaths from flooding in MEDCs is declining yet economic costs are increasing?
2 Outline the differences in the impact of flooding between Bangladesh and another case study you have looked at.

Channel catchment activities and possible sources of conflict

In this section you will be revising:

- **human activities in a river basin**
- **conflicts arising from different uses of the basin**

- **case studies of these aspects of river management.**

Human activities within a river basin can have a positive or negative impact on the processes in the channel. They can also give rise to conflicts between the different uses of the basin area or of the water supplied by the river.

Issues that arise from such activities might include:

- creating artificial sections in the river channel, such as channelisation
- over-extraction of water for domestic supplies, agricultural and/or industrial use
- water quality and/or pollution incidents
- dams and reservoir construction
- management of land use and developments, such as urban area expansion or the alteration of vegetation cover, within the river basin.

Case study: The Murray Darling River basin, south-east Australia – managing water supply and quality

Background information on the Murray Darling River basin

- Average rainfall is highest May–October (33mm) and lowest in January (18.5mm). The lowest rainfall coincides with the summer months and high evaporation rates. The basin is located in the rain shadow of the Great Dividing Range mountain area. There is great variability in rainfall between and within years, creating occasion drought.
- Tributaries in the south, such as the River Murray, receive seasonal discharge from snowmelt.
- Vegetation varies from Eucalyptus forest in the Great Dividing range, to grasslands grazed by cattle and sheep in the central and eastern area, to drought-resistant scrub in the west and central basin area.

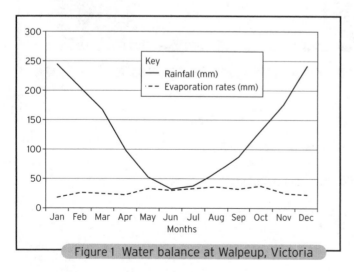

Figure 1 Water balance at Walpeup, Victoria

Issues of changing land use in the river basin area

- Seven of Australia's eight largest cities are dependent on the Murray-Darling River for water, food and/or electricity. Urban areas have grown rapidly in the last 40 years. For example, Canberra has grown from 67,000 population in 1961 to over 325,000 today.
- The river basin contains 42 per cent of Australia's farms and produces a wide range of agricultural products including livestock, fruit, vegetables, rice, cotton, dairy produce and wine. Less than 20 per cent of vegetation is natural and there has been an increase in soil erosion, for example, gully erosion in Victoria. This is due to land being cleared for arable farming with the development of European styles of agriculture plus an increase in grazing by sheep and cattle.
- The Snowy Mountains Scheme created dams and pipelines to transfer water to lower parts of the river basin as well as HEP stations. Irrigation has also been used to support changing styles of agriculture.

Problems of water quality and use

- There is a build up of salt deposits in the soil due to prolonged periods of irrigation. This reduces the range of plants that can be grown and water in the main channel may become unsuitable for human consumption. Higher water tables, such as in the Shepperton area, will lead to a fall of 30 per cent in long term productivity which will have socio-economic effects.
- Eutrophication is encouraged by low levels of water during dry periods, which leads to a concentration of algae, and poor water management.

Management

- Issues of water supply and demand in different sections have resulted in water quotas. Water entitlements can be traded, that is water that is not needed can be sold or an additional quota to expand agricultural activities can be purchased.
- More efficient irrigation techniques have been introduced, such as trickle irrigation or furrow irrigation, which takes water directly to within reach of plant roots.
- Re-planting schemes using native tree species are reducing the downslope movement of water.
- Fencing land and limiting the number of grazing sheep or cattle to within land capacity have been introduced.
- Landcare advisers and local community groups are making farmers more aware of the value of land management and more sustainable techniques.

Case study: Three Gorges Dam, China

Dams are built for a variety of reasons:

- flood control and regulation of a river's regime (flow)
- hydro-electric power (HEP)
- water storage for supply to an urban area.

Details of the Three Gorges scheme

- Located at Sandouping along the Yangtze river (Figure 2).
- Approved in 1992 and is expected to take until at least 2009 to complete, when it will be the largest HEP project in the world. It will supply one-seventh of China's electricity supply.

Reminder

Make sure that you learn some key facts and figures on the different aspects of your supporting case studies.

Key concept

A **mega dam** is a very large dam which is often multipurpose to justify its large construction costs.

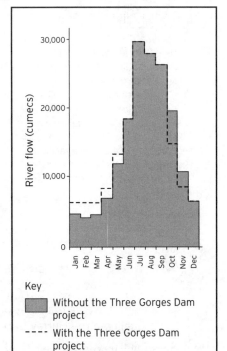

Key

▨ Without the Three Gorges Dam project

‑ ‑ ‑ With the Three Gorges Dam project

Figure 2 Seasonal flow of the Yangtze downstream of the Dam, estimated after the completion of the Dam as well as actual levels for the present

Advantages	Disadvantages
Environmental	**Environmental**
○ Reduced air pollution as HEP replaces the present coal-fired power stations (which currently generate 80 per cent of the country's electricity) ○ Reduced siltation in the lakes in middle and lower reaches of the river	○ Increased pollution from sewage and industrial effluent trapped in the reservoir area which will affect water quality ○ Siltation of the reservoir ○ Increased scour below the dam; larger protection may be needed in the middle reaches ○ A risk of landslips in the reservoir might mean the need for slope stabilisation in some areas, such as at Zigui ○ The reservoir is located on a major geological fault; it will hold so much water that this could trigger an earthquake causing damage to the dam and possible devastating floods in the valley below. However, it has been designed to withstand an earthquake of magnitude 7. ○ Some ecosytems, such as that of the river dolphins, may be affected; the Siberian Crane and the White Flag Dolphin are threatened with extinction ○ A developing tourist industry will be affected as the present breathtaking gorges will cease to exist after the flooding
Socio-economic	**Socio-economic**
○ The dam and river embankments will give improved flood control along the middle and lower reaches, especially in the densely populated areas such as Jingjjang ○ Protection from a one in a hundred year flood ○ HEP (18,200 MW) will provide around 10 per cent of China's current needs and promote economic growth and more jobs in the valley region ○ Navigation will be improved following raised water levels caused by the dam (formerly rapids) and will enable Chongqing to develop as a major port and industrial area ○ The reservoir will provide water for the valley towns and will facilitate the transfer of water to shortage areas such as the Northern Plain	○ Estimated that the river will flood 11 counties, 140 towns, 326 townships and 1351 villages. This will result in the relocation of at least 1.2m people, some into physically more demanding or remote areas ○ Fertile cropland and areas of citrus orchards will be submerged, around 23,800 hectares in total ○ Over 1200 heritage sites, such as the Zhang Fei temple, will be drowned together with some settlements, for example, Fengdu ○ Likely to result in urban migration but some people will lack the skills to move to a new job ○ Loss of family traditions ○ Dam may be a vulnerable target in war or the focus for a terrorist attack

Table 1 Advantages and disadvantages of the scheme

Reminder

You need to learn the costs and benefits of more than one dam, including an example of a mega dam.

Quick check questions

1 What issues are indicated by the water balance graph at Walpeup in the Murray Darling Basin (Figure 1)?

2 Identify some examples of the socio-economic impacts of poor water quality in the Murray Darling river basin.

3 Which groups might come into conflict with the development of the Three Gorges Dam?

A review of management approaches and sustainability

In this section you will be revising:

- river management approaches
- sustainable river management
- case studies of river management.

River management approaches

In a natural river channel there is equilibrium between the different characteristics, such as width, depth and sinuosity, as they adjust to the natural flow regime and discharge of the river. Human activities can alter these characteristics which will cause changes elsewhere (see Figure 1, page 40).

The main reasons for river management are to:

- try to prevent flooding
- manage conflicting demands of water users
- permit activities such as river navigation or the abstraction of water for drinking
- allow sustainable development of the finite supply of water resources.

Such management schemes produce both advantages (benefits) and disadvantages (costs). Developers weigh these up before deciding whether the scheme should go ahead. Such analysis goes beyond the purely financial aspects, to also consider the impacts on the local environment and people (Table 1).

Approach	Methods	Advantages	Disadvantages
Increased storage in the river basin	Dams and reservoirs	Large storage facilities created, plus other benefits such as HEP, fish farming, recreation	Loss of agricultural land and resettlement issues; river may silt up; disruption to river regime and river ecosystems; vulnerable to terrorist attacks or as wartime target
	Terracing	Reduces overland flow by up to 90 per cent; reduces erosion and silting and increases farmland area	Labour intensive to create and maintain
	Afforestation	Reduces overland flow; increases throughflow; river flows are less extreme; other benefits include timber and recreation areas	Labour intensive; takes time for the trees to reach maturity
Increased output from the basin by channelisation (hard engineering, see Figure 1)	Resectioning or realignment of the channel such as straightening, widening or deepening	Reduces friction, improves efficiency and increases river speed; short cuts through long meanders increase the evacuation of water reducing flood levels; can be combined with landscaping to improve amenity value; may increase the gradient of the long profile, increasing river velocity	Destruction of bed and bank habitats; involves compulsory purchase of riverside land which may cause controversy; may lead to localised increase in erosion and a transfer of the problem downstream; possible increase of downstream flooding *(Continued on page 40)*

Table 1 Advantages and disadvantages of river management approaches

Approach	Methods	Advantages	Disadvantages
	Bank protection such as gabions, training walls, wing dykes	Bank protection controls meander migration and prevents bank erosion and land loss; wing dykes encourage sediment to be deposited in the lee of the dykes while increasing velocity and channel depth in the central section, so aiding navigation	Hard engineering is often unsightly and expensive; may lead to localised increase in erosion and a transfer of the problem downstream
	Dredging	Removal of sediment aids navigation and increases river flow thereby reducing risk of flooding	Affects sediment and alluvium levels downstream
Separating people from rivers	Levées	Natural levées are reinforced to contain flood waters	Prevents deposition of silt on the floodplain; sediment is deposited in the channel increasing the level of the river bed and risk of flooding; if levées are over topped the flood water cannot drain back into the river so that floods may be prolonged; can be expensive to maintain
	Diversions	Minimum impact on river ecology and hydrology; relief channels can be used for other purposes such as recreation in non-flood periods	Creates an artificial barrier to urban growth
	Strategic retreat: deliberate movement of people away from risk areas	Removes the risk to people; retains the river's character; no ongoing costs	Initially expensive; depends on finding a suitable alternative location; politically unpopular

Table 1 *Continued*

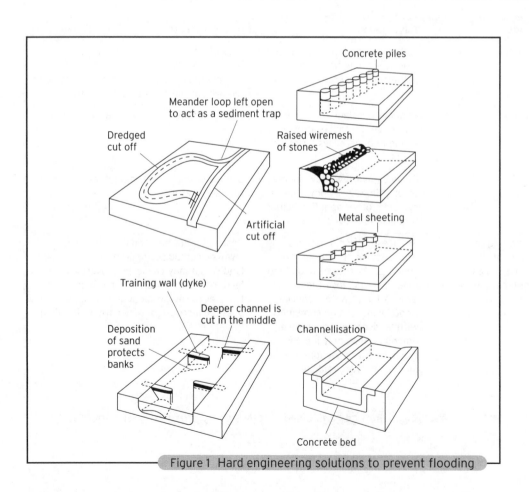

Figure 1 Hard engineering solutions to prevent flooding

Case study: management in the Komadugu-Yobe river basin, north-east Nigeria (LEDC)

- Between June and August in the Komadugu-Yobe river basin, intense tropical rains usually bring floods, while between November and March, river flow drops considerably causing streams to dry up with drought as a possible consequence.
- Since the mid-1960s, average annual rainfall in the area has declined.
- Traditional farming focuses on the renewal of fertile silt deposits with the floodwaters, which enables fruit, vegetables and rice to be grown. Simple irrigation ditches can also provide water for the growth of millet and sorghum in the dry season.
- The Hadejia-Nguru wetlands are an important source of fish and provide grazing land for the semi-nomadic Fulani cattle herders. Migratory birds in this area have also helped the development of tourism.
- Most villagers rely on wells for their water supply; a few use petrol pumps to lift water onto the land.

Two approaches to river management

Hard engineering: A series of dams	Soft engineering: A water conservation project
- Tiga Dam on the Kano River (1974) - Challawa Gorge Dam (1992) - Hadeja River barrage	The Nguru Wetlands Conservation Project
Approach: - Storage of water in a series of dams - Canals and dykes carry water to a total of 25,500 hectares of land - Small motorised pumps, available at subsidised prices, and many tube wells are used to irrigate the land	Approach: - Conserves the value of wetlands both economically and environmentally - Promotes **sustainable development** in the area for people and wildlife - Teaches local people about wetland management - Releases large wet-season flows from the Tiga and Challawa Gorge dams into rivers

Impacts:
- Increased yields of crops, such as rice and a greater variety of fruit and vegetables such as onions, tomatoes and peppers
- Poorer farmers cannot afford the pumps
- Changed patterns of flooding may affect traditional farmers
- Initial jobs created may be replaced by machines
- Fulani cattle herders find it difficult to find grazing areas, as many have been claimed for cultivation, and livestock routes have been blocked
- Fish numbers and species have declined and their movements have been disrupted, affecting fishing livelihoods
- Falling tourist numbers due to the reduction in wetlands and associated bird life
- Fertile alluvium is trapped behind the dams and no longer reaches farmland downstream
	Impacts:
	- Water and fertile alluvium are distributed more fairly
	- Supports the traditional method of irrigation and farming
	- Marsh grazing land is maintained
	- Involves a programme to monitor:
	  – the extent of flooding and of changes in vegetation and wildlife
	  – the use of water from village wells in order to check levels of the water table
	  – competition for land between animal herders and crop farmers
	- Distribution of fuel-efficient wood stoves was designed to reduce wood consumption
	- Helps people to resolve conflicts

Table 2 Two approaches to river management

Key concepts

Sustainable development is development that does not compromise the needs of future generations by current practice. This can be observed on social, economic or environmental criteria.

Integrated river management involves developing a range of management solutions that work together to address a more complex issue.

Sustainable river management. More sustainable river management approaches are now being explored, including the restoration of river environments (Figure 2).

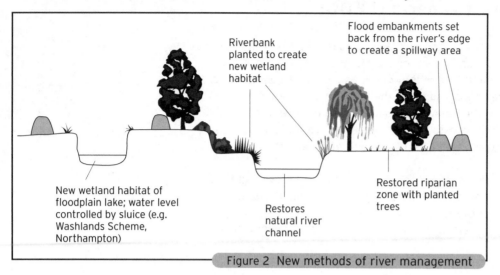

Flood embankments set back from the river's edge to create a spillway area

Riverbank planted to create new wetland habitat

New wetland habitat of floodplain lake; water level controlled by sluice (e.g. Washlands Scheme, Northampton)

Restores natural river channel

Restored riparian zone with planted trees

Figure 2 New methods of river management

Other soft engineering strategies include:

- relief channels constructed to divert high flow away from the main channel, leaving the natural channel intact. For example, the Maidenhead, Windsor and Eton flood alleviation scheme
- partial dredging: dredging or weed clearance to increase the cross-sectional area of the river is focused on shallow riffle sections; aquatic habitats are therefore maintained.

Quick check questions

1 Which management strategy in Table 1 is likely to be the most expensive? Why?

2 Identify the positive and negative impacts of the dams' development in the Komadugu-Yobe river basin.

Reminder

Try to learn the details of several case studies that show different approaches, including hard and soft engineering.

River environments: Exam style questions

1.12

1. Define the following terms: (2 marks each)
   i) drainage basin
   ii) base flow
   iii) saturated overland flow
   iv) river competence
   v) river regime.

2. Explain why the global hydrological cycle is an example of a closed system. (2)

3. Suggest why river channels may become braided. (3)

4. Explain how a change of land use from woodland to agriculture in a large area within a river drainage basin might affect the amount and quality of discharge. (5)

5. Outline the processes at work in a river channel at and below a waterfall. (4)

6. Explain, using examples, why in many regions of the world there is an imbalance between water supply and demand. (6)

7. Study the two hydrographs (Figure 1) below which show the response of two neighbouring rivers of similar size to the same rainstorm.

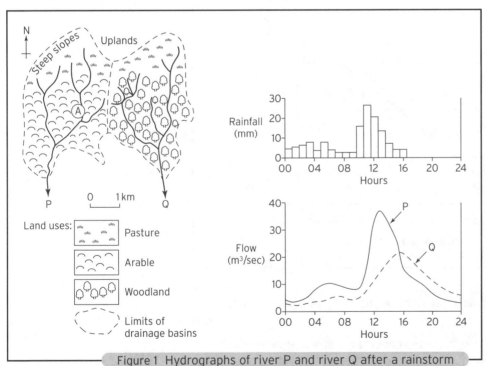

Figure 1 Hydrographs of river P and river Q after a rainstorm

i) For hydrograph Q, work out the peak discharge and the lag time. (2)
ii) Explain why there is a lag time between peak rainfall and peak discharge. (4)
iii) Compare the responses of the two rivers to the rainstorm shown. (4)
iv) Suggest reasons for the differences between the two hydrographs. (4)
v) There are plans to expand a village at site A to develop a new town. Explain how this is likely to affect discharge and sediment levels in river P. (5)

8. Suggest reasons for the changes in discharge and velocity shown in
    Figure 2 below. (6)

Upstream	Downstream
Discharge	
Channel width	
Channel depth	
Average velocity	
Channel bed roughness	
Slope angle (gradient)	

Figure 2

9. Study Figure 3 which shows how river velocity relates to sediment size.
    i)   Identify the largest size of sediment that is being transported at a
         velocity of 10 cm per second. (1)
    ii) During a storm, this velocity increases to 100 cm per second. (1)
    iii) There is a severe drought and the river velocity falls to 1 cm per second.
         Describe what will happen to particles as the velocity falls from
         100 cm per second to 1 cm per second. (3)

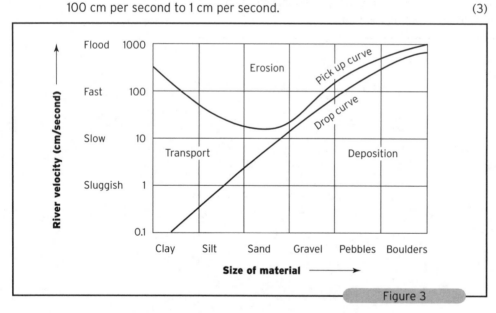

Figure 3

10. For a named river catchment which experiences flooding, examine possible
    strategies for controlling floods. (10)

11. Referring to named examples, examine the importance of wetlands in river
    management. (10)

In this section you will be revising:

- **Coastal zones and beach features**
- **the key features of a coastal environment**
- **an awareness of the interface between river catchments and the sea**

- **the concept of littoral cells and the beach as a system**
- **reasons for coastal change, including the impact of a single storm event.**

A coastline is the boundary between the sea and the land (Figure 1). However, this boundary varies depending on the height of the tide, on a short-term basis, and sea level changes over the longer term. The coastal zone is a broader definition of this boundary. Here there is a combination of terrestrial and **marine processes** to produce a variety of landforms. Human activity and development also influences the character of the coastline.

Key concepts

Marine processes: sea-based processes associated with waves and tidal currents.

Coastal zones and beach features

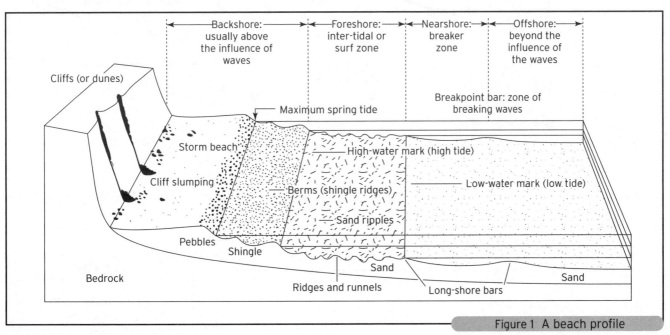

Figure 1 A beach profile

The coast can be seen as an open system with inputs and outputs. The coastal sediment system or **littoral cell** system operates at a variety of scales from a single bay, such as Swanage Bay, to a regional scale, such as the Yorkshire coast. Like any system, changes in factors affect the processes that occur, which in turn affects landscape development. Natural processes are compounded by human impacts such as dams, which affect the sediment supply to the coast (Figure 2), and buildings on the cliff top, which may destabilise the cliff.

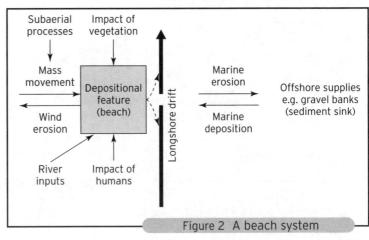

Figure 2 A beach system

Eleven major sediment cells have been identified around the coast of England and Wales. Major cells can also be divided into smaller sub-cells in which there are clear but smaller sediment transfer patterns (for example, see Figure 3).

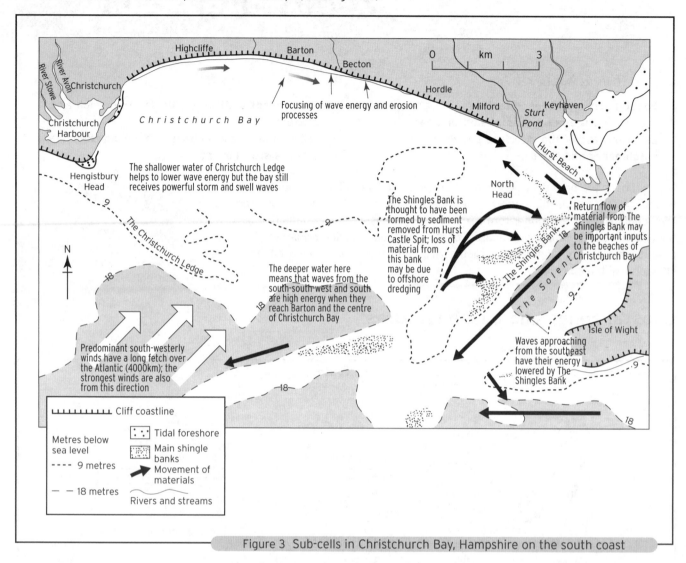

Figure 3 Sub-cells in Christchurch Bay, Hampshire on the south coast

Differing weather conditions and tides can cause short-term changes in the coastal zone, making waves either constructive or destructive (Figure 4 a,b):

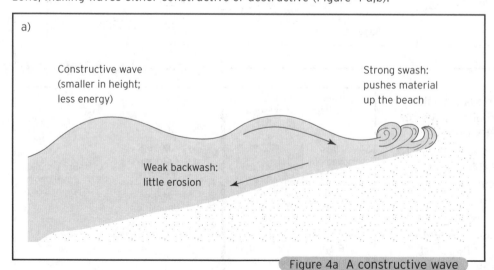

Figure 4a A constructive wave

- Depositional waves which build new features
- Caused by swell from distant storms

Key concepts

The **littoral zone** is the area between the highest and lowest spring tides.
A **littoral cell** is a physical unit with clearly identified sediment pathways, where inputs and outputs are balanced.

Reminder

Learn the details of a specific example of a sediment cell; its inputs, transfers and outputs.

- Also called 'swell' or 'surging' waves
- Low energy waves
- Long **wavelength** (up to 100m)
- Low **wave height** (<1m)
- Low frequency (6–8/minute)
- High **wave period** (one every 8–10 seconds)
- Elliptical **wave orbit**
- Swash > **backwash**
- Much percolation through the sand
- Little transport of sand down the beach
- Low gradient

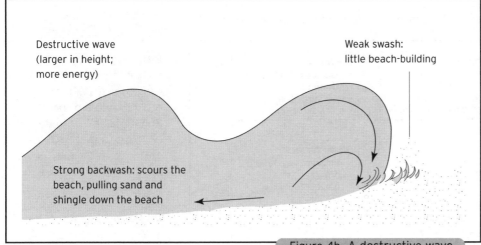

Destructive wave (larger in height; more energy)

Weak swash: little beach-building

Strong backwash: scours the beach, pulling sand and shingle down the beach

Figure 4b A destructive wave

- Erosional waves that remove beach material
- Caused by local winds and storms
- Also called 'surfing', 'storm' or 'plunging' waves
- High energy waves
- Short **wavelength** (<20m)
- High **wave height** (>1m)
- High frequency (10–12/minute)
- Low **wave period** (one every 5–6 seconds)
- Circular **wave orbit**
- **Backwash** > **swash**
- Little percolation through the sand
- Much transport of sand down the beach
- Steep gradient

Storm activity tends to result in:

- rapid erosion
- flooding in low level areas
- storm beaches
- landslides and rockfalls in the backshore zone.

Storm surges occur when storms and high tides coincide making the high tide even higher. The effects of these in low-lying areas such as Bangladesh may be exaggerated by a funnel-shaped coastline.

Reminder

For more details on coastal flooding see Section 1.19: A review of management strategies (page 67).

Quick check questions

1 Outline how the beach system operates.

2 Describe the sediment movement in Christchurch Bay and explain the impact of dredging the Shingles Bank.

Factors and processes affecting landforms

In this section you will be revising:

- the physical factors and processes that influence coastal landforms
- coastal landforms that result from these processes
- a case study of an extended (40–50km) stretch of coastline.

A variety of physical and human factors influence the nature of the coastline (Figure 1).

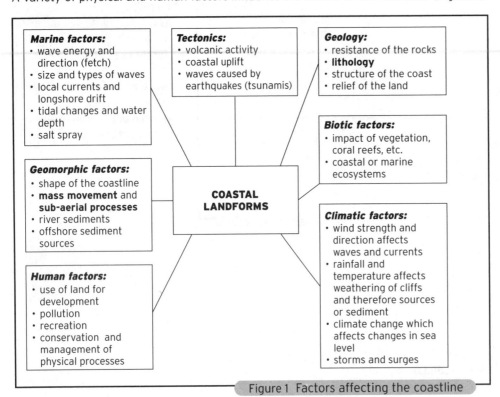

Marine factors:
- wave energy and direction (fetch)
- size and types of waves
- local currents and longshore drift
- tidal changes and water depth
- salt spray

Tectonics:
- volcanic activity
- coastal uplift
- waves caused by earthquakes (tsunamis)

Geology:
- resistance of the rocks
- **lithology**
- structure of the coast
- relief of the land

Biotic factors:
- impact of vegetation, coral reefs, etc.
- coastal or marine ecosystems

Geomorphic factors:
- shape of the coastline
- **mass movement** and **sub-aerial processes**
- river sediments
- offshore sediment sources

COASTAL LANDFORMS

Climatic factors:
- wind strength and direction affects waves and currents
- rainfall and temperature affects weathering of cliffs and therefore sources or sediment
- climate change which affects changes in sea level
- storms and surges

Human factors:
- use of land for development
- pollution
- recreation
- conservation and management of physical processes

Figure 1 Factors affecting the coastline

Waves and tides

Waves are usually generated by wind blowing over the sea surface, although some waves, tsunamis, are caused by earthquakes (see Figure 2).

Waves are caused by different layers of air in the wind travelling at different speeds.

1. The layer closest to the sea surface exerts a frictional drag on the water yet also exerts a drag on the air layer above it.
2. The highest 'layers' of air have the least drag on them and therefore move faster than the ones closer to the sea surface.
3. As a result, the air tumbles forward and finally develops a circular motion. This motion exerts downwards pressure (DP) on the sea surface at its front and upward pressure (UP) at its rear. This means the surface begins to take on the form of a wave.
4. The wind continues to press on the back of the developing wave causing it to steepen.

Key concepts

Lithology: the character of rock; its structure, composition, texture and resistance to erosion.
Sub-aerial: a feature that occurs, or a process that operates, on the Earth's surface rather than underground or under the sea.
Mass movement: the downslope movement of weathered material under the influence of gravity.

Key concepts

Fetch: the length of open sea over which a wind blows to generate waves.
Tidal range: the vertical difference between high and low tide.
Amphidromic point: places where there is no tidal range.
Wave refraction: when waves approach an irregular coastline. This reduces wave velocity.

Wave energy is affected by:

- wind strength and duration
- **fetch** and the length of time the wind has been blowing over the sea
- depth of the sea bed.

In the UK, the maximum fetch is west and south west across the Atlantic; the North Sea has a lower fetch.

Tides and the tidal cycle

Tides are regular movements in the sea's surface, caused by the gravitational pull of the Moon and the Sun on the oceans. Spring tides occur when the Sun and Moon are aligned with the Earth. Low spring tides occur after a new Moon; high spring tides occur after a full Moon. Neap tides occur when the Sun and Moon are at right angles to the Earth.

Tides are influenced by:

- the size and shape of the ocean basins. For example, the tidal range is greatest in bays and funnel-shaped coastlines
- the characteristics of the shoreline
- the Coriolis Force caused by the Earth's rotation. For example, in the Northern hemisphere, water is deflected to the right of its path, hence tides in the Britain are higher than in Ireland
- meteorological conditions. For example, during low pressure systems, water levels are raised 10cm for every decrease in pressure of 10mb.

The **tidal range** is also important as:

- it controls the vertical range of erosion and deposition
- weathering is affected by the time between tides
- velocity increases with the tidal range and has an important scouring effect.

Tidal range can be used to classify coastal areas (Table 1).

Category	Tidal range	Example
Microtidal	Low (<2m)	Mediterranean Sea
Mesotidal	Medium (2–4m)	Western coast of USA
Macrotidal	High (>4m)	UK

Table 1 Classification of coastal areas by tidal range

When waves approach parallel to the shore a cell circulation with rip currents develops as the backwash becomes more concentrated by variations in the beach surface. This 'undertow' flow can scour a channel and/or result in the development of minor beach landforms, such as beach cusps

Longshore drift. This is the movement of sediment along the coast by wave action. The phases of longshore drift are as follows.

1   When the waves approach the shore at an angle, material is pushed up the beach by the swash of the breaking wave in the same direction as the wave approaches.
2   As the water returns down the beach, the backwash drags materials more directly down the steepest gradient which is generally at right angles to the beach line.
3   Over a period of time, sediment moves in a zig-zag pattern down the coast.
4   Obstacles such as groynes interfere with this drift and an accumulation of sediment occurs on the 'updrift' side.

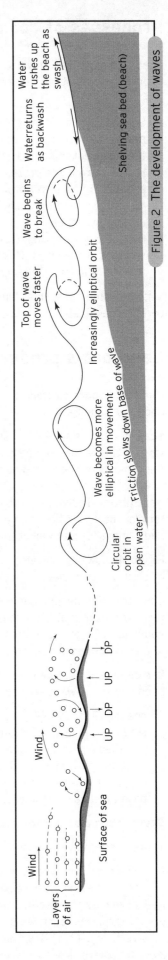

Figure 2 The development of waves

Processes of coastal erosion

There are a number of ways in which coasts are eroded (Figure 3). In addition, there are several forms of weathering.

- Salt weathering is the process by which sodium and magnesium compounds expand in joints and cracks thereby weakening rock structures.
- Freeze-thaw is the process whereby water freezes, expands and breaks down jointed rocks.
- Water layer weathering is the tidal cycle of wetting and drying (hydration).
- Biological weathering is carried out by molluscs, sponges and urchins. This form of weathering is important in low energy coasts.

Mass movements, such as landslides, are also common on certain coastlines.

Landforms produced by erosion

Cliffs and shore platforms. For example, Three Cliffs Bay and Limeslade Bay.

Sea cliffs can be thought of as normal slopes, except that wave action erodes the base of the cliff as well as aiding the removal of weathered material. If there is a build up of material at the base of the cliff, the cliff is protected from wave attack. The wave energy is then used in attrition of this debris to a suitable size for transport. The balance between mass movement of material down the cliff face and removal of material at the base is important in determining the form of the cliff.

Figure 4 shows the development of a wave-cut platform as the cliff face recedes through wave erosion.

Cliff formation depends on the nature of the rocks and their resistance to erosion, rock structure (that is the make up of different layers and whether they dip or are folded), and the position of any lines of weakness such as fault lines.

It is important to remember that not all sea cliffs have been caused by wave erosion. Other causes include:

- changes in sea level: the cliff may be simply the steep slopes of the land which have been further modified by subsequent marine erosion
- faulting which may result in a steep face of rock dropping steeply into the sea. For example, the basalt cliffs along the eastern coast of Skye.

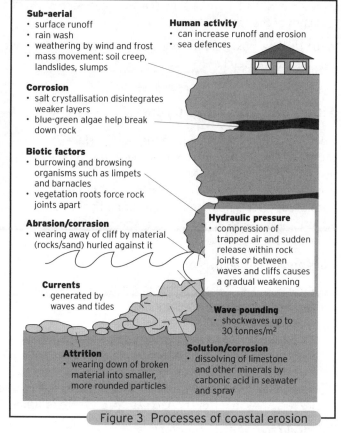

Figure 3 Processes of coastal erosion

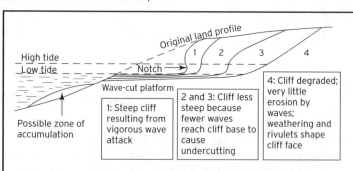

Figure 4 The formation of a wave-cut platform

Caves, blowholes, arches and stacks. For example, Worms Head and Mumbles Head.

These micro-features form during the retreat of a headland (see Figure 5, page 51):

1 When cliffs in hard rock are subject to marine erosion, caves may be formed if there is some local weakness such as a jointed or faulted zone. Sometimes a cave may collapse to produce a narrow inlet known as a geo.
2 Many caves reach the surface some distance inland as a vertical pit cut along a vertical joint. This is called a blow hole
3 If a cave is eroded into the side of a headland, or one from either side, an arch is formed.

4   The arch then collapses, leaving the seaward section standing as a stack.
5   With time these stacks become worn by waves and sometimes collapse. They are then known as stumps. These roughly indicate the extent of the former headland until they are removed completely by wave erosion.

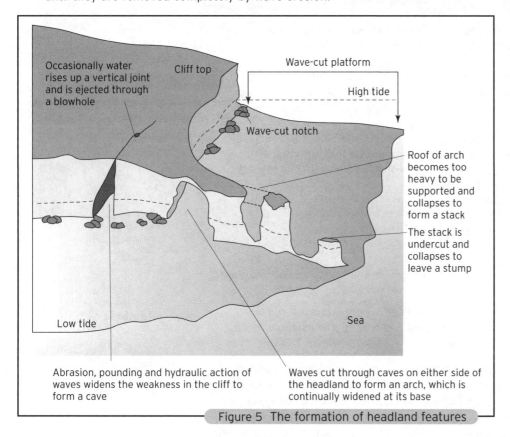

Occasionally water rises up a vertical joint and is ejected through a blowhole

Cliff top

Wave-cut platform

High tide

Wave-cut notch

Roof of arch becomes too heavy to be supported and collapses to form a stack

The stack is undercut and collapses to leave a stump

Low tide

Sea

Abrasion, pounding and hydraulic action of waves widens the weakness in the cliff to form a cave

Waves cut through caves on either side of the headland to form an arch, which is continually widened at its base

Figure 5 The formation of headland features

Processes and landforms of coastal deposition

Sediment is deposited when waves and currents slow down, or the supply of sediment exceeds the rate of removal. Sediment size influences this process. Pebbles are deposited when the wave energy is relatively high, but much smaller particles, such as clay and silt, can be transported by low energy waves and currents.

Essential requirements for deposition include:

- a large supply of material
- longshore drift
- an irregular, indented coastline including river mouths
- low energy coastlines
- bioconstruction (that is the work of plants).

Beaches. For example, Oxwich Bay. As waves approach the shore, water depth usually decreases. When the depth of the water is less than half the wavelength, friction with the seabed increases. This causes waves to slow down and their length decreases. At the same time the height and steepness of the wave increases until the upper part of the wave spills or plunges over. As the wave breaks, surf runs up the beach in a movement called swash. The return flow is backwash.

The way in which a wave breaks and whether it is a constructive or destructive wave affects the form of the beach. There are two common beach forms (Table 2).

Swash-aligned beaches:	Drift-aligned beaches:
• occur when waves arrive at right angles to the shore or are turned to face the shore by wave refraction • are common in bays between headlands • offshore bars of sand, moved from the beach, form near to the low tide level • localised water movements on the beach produce smaller-scale features such as runnels, rip channels and beach cusps • where the sediment size is larger, the profile of the beach becomes steeper and percolation is faster • berm ridges are formed by the waves at high tide; during winter storms these can become large and steep.	• occur when the waves approach at an angle to the beach • are characteristic of straighter coastlines where longshore drift is common. • waves approaching the shore at 30° create the greatest amount of drift. • spits form where there is a change of direction in the coastline or at a river mouth where the main coastal drift is cut short by the main river channel.

Table 2 Beach forms

Spits and bars. For example, Whitford Spit. Wave refraction, tidal currents or changing winds can recurve spits towards the main shoreline. For example, Hurst Castle spit or Spurn Head (see also Figure 6).

Barrier beaches are elongated offshore bars, parallel to the coast and separated by a lagoon. They are distinct from beaches and remain above sea level even at high tide. They are mostly found in gently sloping, low-lying areas where wave energy is low. One theory is that they may have been developed as sand dunes and beach ridges that became separated from the mainland by the rising sea levels of the past 10,000 years. Examples of barrier beaches are Chesil Beach and Slapton Ley. The action of storm waves periodically washing water and sediment over the island beaches causes the barrier islands to gradually migrate landwards.

Reminder

For details of deltas and their formation see section 1.6 (pages 24–5).

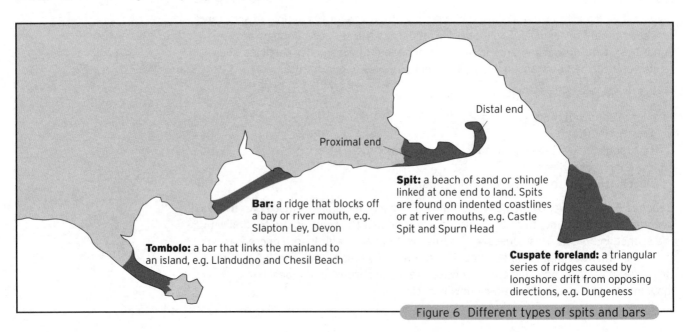

Bar: a ridge that blocks off a bay or river mouth, e.g. Slapton Ley, Devon

Tombolo: a bar that links the mainland to an island, e.g. Llandudno and Chesil Beach

Spit: a beach of sand or shingle linked at one end to land. Spits are found on indented coastlines or at river mouths, e.g. Castle Spit and Spurn Head

Cuspate foreland: a triangular series of ridges caused by longshore drift from opposing directions, e.g. Dungeness

Proximal end

Distal end

Figure 6 Different types of spits and bars

Mud flats and coastal marshes. Tides tend to deposit fine silts along gently-sloping coasts, especially in bays and estuaries. These silts, together with river alluvium, result in the build up of a platform of mud known as a mudflat. Salt-tolerant plants soon begin to colonise the mudflat, which in time becomes marshland. Mudflats are usually crossed by winding channels kept clear of vegetation by tidal actions. At low tides these channels often contain little, if any, water.

Sand dunes. For example, Whitford Burrows. The largest sand dunes are found in mid-latitude storm wave environments, promoted by:

- a large supply of sand on the beach
- high onshore wind speeds
- low precipitation
- low humidity.

A large tidal range will also expose more sand, especially if the beach slope gradient is low. Consequently, sand dunes are found on all British coasts, but they are more sparsely distributed in the south and south east.

Quick check questions

1 If Cornwall faces the highest energy waves from the Atlantic, why does the area not experience high rates of erosion?

2 Which of the processes in Figure 3 would you identify as cliff face processes and which cliff foot processes?

3 Look at Figure 1 which summarises the factors that influence coastlines. Which of these factors might also affect the rate of erosion of a coastline?

4 Try to think of named examples of each of the erosional and depositional coastal features outlined in this section.

Reminder

For more details on sand dunes see section 1.15 Coastal ecosystems and the impact of human activities (pages 54–6).

Reminder

Look at page 98 in *Changing Environments*, Heinemann 2000 for details of how the geology of Collywell Bay, Northumberland has influence the form of the coast.

1.15 Coastal ecosystems and the impact of human activities

In this section you will be revising:

- **the changes that result in coastal ecosystems from natural change, to include the concept of succession**
- **the direct and indirect impact of human activities on ecosystems**

- **case studies of a sand dune ecosystem contrasted with a different coastal ecosystem, a salt marsh, including factors affecting distribution**
- **awareness of fieldwork techniques to study succession and human impacts.**

Coastal ecosystems can experience change through natural change and through direct or indirect impact of human activities.

Case study of a sand dune ecosystem (psammosere), Studland Heath, Dorset

> **Key concept**
>
> **Succession**: a series of changes which take place in a plant community.

The development of sand dunes starts with onshore winds moving sand grains by saltation. Irregularities in the surface of the sand then produce eddying causing material to be deposited on the leeward side. Thereafter **succession** takes place towards the climatic climax vegetation (Figure 1).

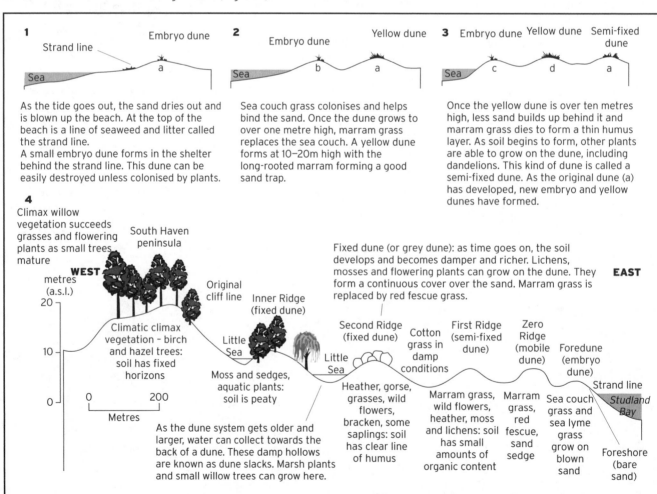

Figure 1 Sand dune succession at Studland Heath

In a sand dune, the biomass or amount of living matter is generally low because the dunes are continually moving. However, biomass and Net Primary Productivity (the rate of increase of biomass) increases with distance from the sea, as conditions become less harsh and soil depth increases.

Trophic levels in a typical sand dune ecosystem

Distinct vegetation communities are found moving landward from the seaward dune edge with the changing environmental conditions. The climax vegetation found depends largely on the nature of the soil. If there is a high proportion of shells (providing calcium), grasslands are often found. In contrast, acid soils are found on old dunes where the calcium has been leached out and heathers and ling dominate. Pine trees favour acid soils, but oak trees need more neutral soils.

Destruction of vegetation, exposing the underlying sand to wind, often causes a blowout. Once this starts, the edges of the blowout may continue to erode, resulting in extensive areas of open sand within what was previously a stabilised area. However, blowouts are an important part of the dynamic dune system since they create new niches for flora and fauna (Figure 2).

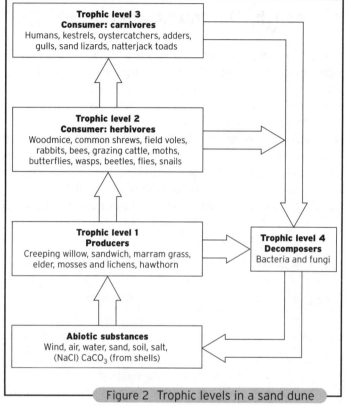

Figure 2 Trophic levels in a sand dune

Human threats to sand dunes

Pressures on Studland Heath include:

- visitor pressure: on a busy day in summer up to 25,000 people visit Studland
- the vast majority come to the beach but some also visit the sand dunes and nature reserve
- the number of visitors is increasing each year
- dune and vegetation erosion caused by people walking through the dunes to the beach or for shelter, threatening plant and animal species and their breeding grounds
- traffic congestion in car parks and roads leading to the area; over 220,000 cars park annually which also results in noise and air pollution and is a hazard to animals
- over twelve tonnes of litter is left per week by visitors; if left outside the bins provided this is dangerous to small animals and birds
- sun tan oil washed up on the beach can affect the dunes at high tide
- heath fires destroy plants and animals at least once a year. The most common cause is discarded cigarette ends. Lizards and snakes can escape by burrowing but may not escape predators once vegetation cover has gone.

Management strategies introduced by the National Trust and English Nature at Studland since 1982 include:

- enlarging the four main car parks and increasing their capacity by 800
- building a visitor centre with shop, cafe, and information point to educate visitors to the value of this ecosystem and the need to take care of it
- increasing the number of toilets; adding facilities for the disabled
- closing some footpaths and fencing part of the dunes for conservation
- laying out more hard-wearing surfaces along key sections of footpaths to reduce erosion
- planting marram grass to stabilise blowouts and other dune areas
- placing litter bins on paths and at the back of the beach
- placing fire beaters on the heather and gorse heath as well as fire breaks and water hydrants

Key concept

Seral stages: the different recognisable stages within a succession.

Reminder

See pages 124–129 of *Changing Environments*, Heinemann 2000 for more details on Studland Heath and information on the fieldwork techniques used to study natural change (succession) and human impacts in a sand dune environment.

- erecting information boards to educate people about the area and the reasons why there is restricted access to conservation areas
- employing wardens to supervise the conservation and restoration work and the use of the area by the public. As part of their duties, they are able to explain to people how they can avoid damaging the area.

Case study of a salt marsh ecosystem (halosere), Alnmouth, Northumberland

Salt marshes are common around the coast of Britain. Alnmouth is the largest salt marsh in the north east of England and is managed by the National Trust. Salt marshes develop in sheltered areas where deposition is possible (see Figures 3 and 4) and where salt water and fresh water meet, as in estuaries and lagoons. They tend to:

- be covered by water at high tide and exposed at low tide
- contain halophytes: plants that can tolerate saline (salty) conditions
- experience a fluctuation of tides which results in large amounts of silt being deposited both by the ebb tide and by the river as it meets the sea
- be colonised initially by green algae and eel grass
- follow a succession after this initial stage (Figure 3, page 57)
- contain salt pans in certain parts of the upper marsh area in which conditions are too salty for plants to survive.

Human impacts on salt marshes at Almouth Bay are shown in Table 1.

Area of impact	Examples of impacts
Farming	- Unlike other saltmarsh areas, no livestock grazing is allowed in the area, because it leads to the selective removal of certain grass species, such as red fescue. However, rabbits spill over from the nearby sand dunes and damage vegetation, which has a dwarfing effect on the plants. - The addition of chemical fertilisers to the surrounding farmland alters the natural composition of the marsh. - Some areas of the marsh have been reclaimed and drained for ploughing and crop growing. - Alteration to the course of rivers or natural drainage may also affect water levels and pathways.

Tourism	- Growth in tourism, both day trips and longer holidays, has resulted in increased trampling through the sand dunes. Horse riders and walkers also cross the marsh at times, trampling the vegetation.
	- Vehicles are a threat because they gain access to the beach by using the track that runs along the southern edge of the salt marsh. Management of the Alnmouth Bay saltmarsh operates a non-interventionist approach which includes:
	  - maintaining the 'no grazing' rule for domestic animals
	  - signs to indicate to visitors the delicate nature of the ecosystem
	  - regular surveys, carried out by the National Trust and English Nature who are responsible for the saltmarsh as a designated SSSI site.

Table 1 Human impacts on Alnmouth Bay

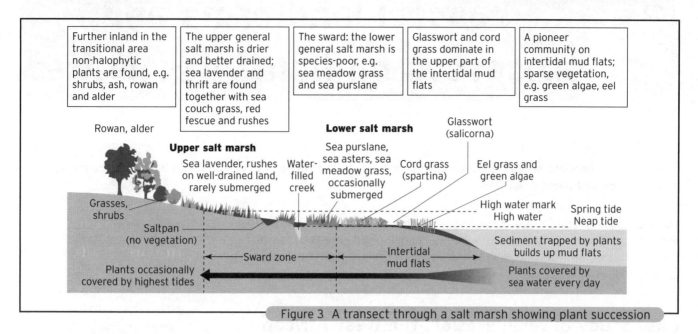

Further inland in the transitional area non-halophytic plants are found, e.g. shrubs, ash, rowan and alder

The upper general salt marsh is drier and better drained; sea lavender and thrift are found together with sea couch grass, red fescue and rushes

The sward: the lower general salt marsh is species-poor, e.g. sea meadow grass and sea purslane

Glasswort and cord grass dominate in the upper part of the intertidal mud flats

A pioneer community on intertidal mud flats; sparse vegetation, e.g. green algae, eel grass

Figure 3 A transect through a salt marsh showing plant succession

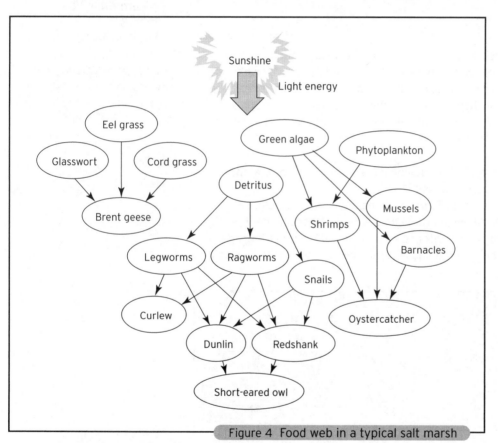

Figure 4 Food web in a typical salt marsh

Quick check questions

1 How might human threats affect the sand dune ecosystem?

2 What other strategies could be used to manage visitor pressure on Studland Heath?

3 How could you measure what impact people are having on the salt marsh ecosystem?

In this section you will be revising:

- short-term impacts of rapid erosion, changing deposition and coastal flooding

- a range of case studies to illustrate the issues.

These changes can be short-term or long-term. Short-term changes include rapid erosion, changing depositional environments, changing delta areas or coastal flooding. Human activities can help to manage such risks but coastal development can also exacerbate the issue.

Case study of rapid erosion, the West African coastline

- Most of the West African coast (Figure 1) is made up of a shallow sandy shoreline consisting of large stretches of sand embankments (created by sand blown onshore or transported along the shore by longshore drift), which have closed off and are separated from the shore by a chain of lakes, lagoons and mangrove swamps.
- The area is prone to storms and has a fetch of over 4000 km, which means that high energy waves easily erode the fine sands of the coastal bed almost permanently.
- This is exaggerated by onshore winds and January and July monsoon winds, which create a west to east coastal current.
- Artificial harbours and ports, such as Tema in Ghana, have been developed to accommodate large ships, with budding trade and economic development. Such artificial structures affect longshore drift and trap sediment destined for further down the coast. Ships also rely on dredging central channels, which further adds to the erosion issue.

> **Reminder**
>
> Look at pages 118–123 in *Changing Environments*, Heinemann 2000 for more details on the West African case study.

> **Reminder**
>
> For more information on the nature of risk and hazards look at section 1.1, page 8.

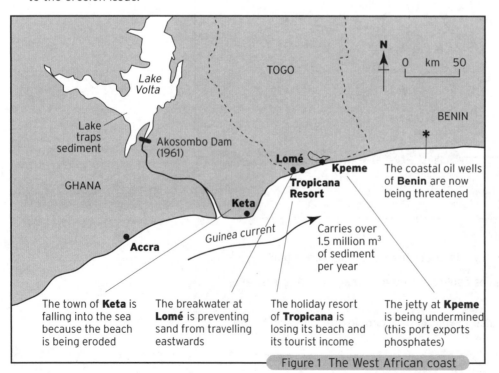

Figure 1 The West African coast

Keta is located on the edge of the River Volta delta on the coast of Ghana. After the Volta Dam was constructed at Akosombo in 1961, the delta area, called Cape St Paul, was realigned. Erosion is occurring at Keta because sediment moved by longshore drift, (which moves up to one million m³ of sediment per year) is deposited first at the Cape. Retreat is at a rate of 8m/yr and has resulted in:
- a loss of property
- the loss of a major road between Keta and Togo
- residents moving away to other areas
- destruction of the town's fishing industry.

Case study of coastal flooding, Towyn, North Wales

The flood occurred on 26 February 1990.

A deep depression (951mb) together with 70 knot onshore winds and a high tide produced a storm surge that overtopped and later breached the seawall embankment.

Five thousand people had to be evacuated from their homes.

Approximately 2800 properties were flooded; many of these were bungalows and 31 per cent of the inhabitants were elderly.

Caravans and other holiday facilities were also badly damaged.

Electric pumps at many sewage stations failed due to the floodwater resulting in the contamination of floodwater with sewage.

The main pumping station that drains surface water was similarly affected which delayed removal of the floodwaters.

40 per cent of those affected did not have adequate house contents insurance and 6 per cent did not have any insurance at all.

Quick check questions

1 How is coastal erosion likely to affect the everyday lives of people at Keta?

2 The flooding in Towyn was said to be an event with a 1 in 500 recurrence level. What does this mean?

The impact of changing sea levels and longer-term changes

In this section you will be revising:

- **longer-term impacts of global climate change on rising sea level (eustatic/ isostatic)**
- **case studies of issues associated with rising sea levels in a number of coastal environments.**

Changing sea levels result in a different set of landforms to those formed by erosion and deposition. Falling sea levels result in, for example, a new floodplain (see Figure 1).

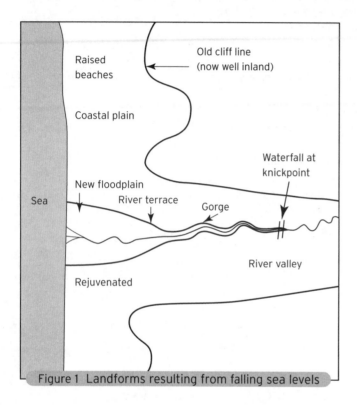

Figure 1 Landforms resulting from falling sea levels

Landforms that result from rising sea levels are:

- Fjord: a steep-sided submerged glaciated valley, e.g. Loch Torridan
- Ria: a steep-sided drowned river valley, e.g. River Fal
- **Estuary**, e.g. Thames Estuary
- Submerged forest, e.g. fossil evidence, Swansea Bay

Features associated with sea level change

The Gower Peninsula, South Wales is a good study area for:

- Raised beach deposits: Limeslade Bay (Figure 2, page 61)
- Raised wave-cut platforms: Limeslade Bay
- Fossil forest (now submerged) showing 'recent' rise in sea level following the end of the last Ice Age: Swansea Bay
- Fossil cliff lines: north and south Gower coast

Key concepts

Eustatic changes: sea level changes that usually result from the fall or rise in global temperatures, which produces a relative fall or rise in the level of the water.

Isostatic changes occur when the land rises or falls relative to the sea water level. This is due to tectonic activity, for example mountain building close to plate boundaries, or when areas experience uplift after an ice sheet has melted.

Estuary: the area of a lower course river, or river mouth, which is affected by tidal change. Estuaries are formed by the post-glacial rise of sea level and the drowning of former lower course river valley areas.

Global warming, both natural and caused by human activities, could mean:

- a faster rate in the rise of the sea level
- an increase in the likelihood of tropical storms
- higher water temperatures
- increased atmospheric carbon dioxide and shallow water may become more acidic.

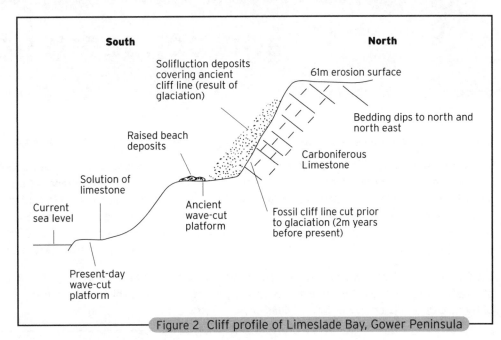

Figure 2 Cliff profile of Limeslade Bay, Gower Peninsula

Case study of changing deposition and rising sea levels in the barrier islands, North Carolina, USA

- These coastal barrier islands are part of a 2700 km feature from Texas to Maine, with 400 distinct islands.
- This coastal barrier complex is continually changing in response to environmental conditions but is in equilibrium when there is a balance between:
  - beach sand
  - energy inputs from waves, tidal currents and hurricanes
  - sea level changes
  - the width gradient of the beach.
- The shoreline of these barrier islands is eroding, beaches are becoming narrower and steeper, and the whole system is migrating landward, for example, 4m per year at Cape Hatteras on Bodie Island.
- Rising sea levels are exaggerating the problem.
- In the natural state, such barrier islands restore themselves from offshore bars and dune systems and vegetation re-colonises overwash areas. However, many of these islands have undergone human development including tourist resorts, such as Kill Devil Hills, roads, utilities and airports.
- This development has created management issues that now require hard engineering such as sea walls, sandbag revetments and groynes to prevent erosion, together with beach nourishment schemes and the use of artificial seaweed to assist beach replenishment, such as was used at Cape Hatteras to protect the lighthouse there. However, these are not sustainable options.

QUICK CHECK Quick check questions

1 Describe how rising sea levels result in each of the following features:
  - fjord
  - ria
  - estuary
  - submerged forest (see Figure 1).

2 Outline how changing sea levels in Limeslade Bay have produced certain features shown in Figure 2.

3 How might rising sea levels exaggerate the problems at Cape Hatteras?

Human activities, conflicts and consequences

In this section you will be revising:

- **how human activities have influenced coastal environments and what are the consequences**
- **details of coastal land uses on an extended coast, including conflicts between activities**

- **case studies from countries, at contrasting states of development, of one of the following:**
  - **urban and industrial development and issues of water quality**
  - **recreational and tourism pressure**
  - **land reclamation schemes.**

Coasts are increasingly coming under pressure from human activities and many sections of coastline are becoming overcrowded, overdeveloped and/or over-exploited. Examples of the negative impacts of human activities on the coastline are shown in Figure 1.

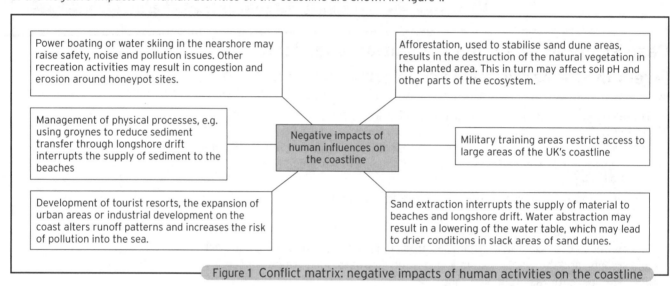

Power boating or water skiing in the nearshore may raise safety, noise and pollution issues. Other recreation activities may result in congestion and erosion around honeypot sites.

Afforestation, used to stabilise sand dune areas, results in the destruction of the natural vegetation in the planted area. This in turn may affect soil pH and other parts of the ecosystem.

Management of physical processes, e.g. using groynes to reduce sediment transfer through longshore drift interrupts the supply of sediment to the beaches

Negative impacts of human influences on the coastline

Military training areas restrict access to large areas of the UK's coastline

Development of tourist resorts, the expansion of urban areas or industrial development on the coast alters runoff patterns and increases the risk of pollution into the sea.

Sand extraction interrupts the supply of material to beaches and longshore drift. Water abstraction may result in a lowering of the water table, which may lead to drier conditions in slack areas of sand dunes.

Figure 1 Conflict matrix: negative impacts of human activities on the coastline

However, human activities can also have positive impacts. One example is the conservation of sand dune areas and associated ecosystems through restrictions on visitor numbers and access, and the appointment of wardens to promote the value of the area and to educate visitors.

Over-exploitation and tourism pressure in coral reefs

Coral reefs are located within the tropics, between latitudes 30° north and 30° south (see Table 1, page 63). Within this zone, however, they are only found at specific locations that meet their exact requirements.

- Water temperature of >18°C. The best conditions for reef development occur between 23–25°C. Temperatures above 27°C also causes problems.
- Clear water, usually <25m deep on the margins of continents or islands, so that sunlight can filter through for photosynthesis and so that their feeding mechanisms do not become clogged up. The shallow water also allows tiny photosynthesising algae to thrive. Symbiosis provides them and the coral with 'food'.
- Areas of strong wave action, as coral reefs thrive in well oxygenated water, but not too exposed to storm conditions that may destroy the delicate coral.

> **Reminder**
>
> A **conflict matrix** can be used to assess whether activities and interests that exist in an area of coastline, complement or conflict with one another.

- Corals are marine creatures that cannot tolerate water salinity of <30–32psu. The exception to this is the highly saline conditions, (+42psu) in the Red Sea or the Persian Gulf, which they will tolerate.
- Limits to the level of the lowest tide as corals die if they are exposed to air for too long.

Types of coral reef	Formation
Fringing reef	Grow around newly-formed islands. These islands subside or sea level rises relative to the land
Barrier reef	If the above process is slow, the reef will grow upwards to form a larger barrier reef separated from the island by a deeper lagoon
Atoll	Forms when the island disappears under the sea. Corals can continue to grow on the surface. Inside the atoll, where the land previously was, there is now calm water and sedimentation

Table 1 Types of coral reef

Energy flow in a reef ecosystem

Natural threats to coral reefs include:

- an increase in water temperature of only 1–2°C, due to short-term and localised El Niño impacts or longer-term climatic change, can lead to the coral reef becoming stressed and turning white or bleached
- disease or predators, such as plagues of the Crown of Thorns starfish in the Great Barrier Reef in Australia, can kill 80–90 per cent of coral-building corals
- extreme weather, such as hurricanes, can result in storm waves that can destroy large areas of coral, or bring large quantities of silt from other areas or from the land that can also damage the coral, for example, tropical storm Debbie, September 1994 in St Lucia.

Human threats to coral reefs include direct and indirect effects of tourism (see Figure 3), which is currently occurring in Thailand, the South Pacific and the Caribbean.

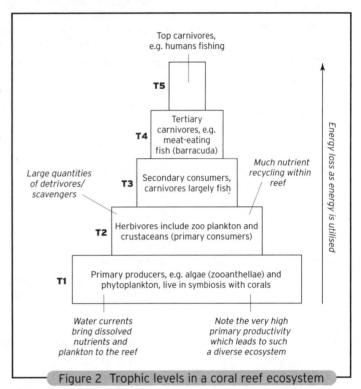

Figure 2 Trophic levels in a coral reef ecosystem

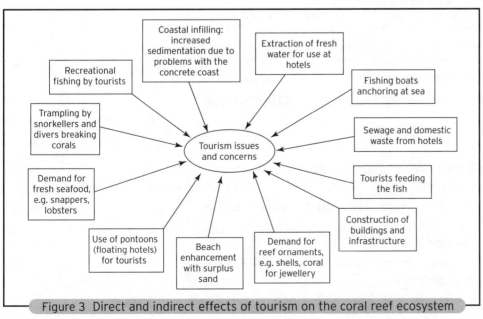

Figure 3 Direct and indirect effects of tourism on the coral reef ecosystem

Other human threats include:

- pollution through oil and industrial outfall, nutrient enrichment and use of chemical fertilisers, such as in the Gulf region
- coral mining for building material, for example in the Philippines
- fishing, which may involve the use of trawling, trophic level disturbance, poisoning (cyanide) and blast fishing, for example in the Phillippines and Indonesia
- global warming and ozone depletion.

Case study: Ban Don Bay coral reefs, Thailand

Main threats:	Management:
Intensive fishing The use of destructive fishing methods such as dynamite fishing Sedimentation due to deforestation and from waste water associated with coastal development Pollution from urban and industrial areas Tourism in heavily visited areas, (7m people now holiday in Thailand, a 64-fold increase in 30 years) Boat moorings in reef areas	Establishing a pilot marine park, such as Muh Koh Ang Tong National Park, where fees are charged for entry, souvenirs and boat permits. The money is then used to develop more sustainable management methods. This will also involve the use of different zones from general access to restricted sanctuary areas, for example, sanctuary at Ko Taen and conservation zones at Ko Samui Creation of an international heritage park and therefore collective ownership Blast and dynamite fishing have been banned (but some people from outside the area continue) Upgrading of law enforcement on illegal fishing Fisheries are to be maintained in a sustainable way through stock enhancement, the development of under-used varieties of coral life, e.g. sea cucumbers and molluscs, and the development of special breeding grounds for ornamental shells to avoid over exploitation of natural stocks Mooring buoys used to mark the location of the reefs to boats, e.g. at Ko Taen Further research into coral reefs A co-ordinated and bottom-up approach to management; that is with the support and involvement of local people Information and visitor centre and trained guides to raise public awareness A trained team will visit villages and schools in an educational campaign Monitoring water quality and legislation drawn up to prohibit damaging construction, especially in areas adjacent to sanctuary zones; sewage outlets will be placed downflow from reef areas Mandatory Environmental Impact Assessments (EIAs) for any coastal resort development which might affect the reef Sustainable use rather than prohibited altogether

Table 2 Threats to and management of the Ban Don Bay coral reefs

Reminder

For more detail on the management of coral reefs, see pages 135–143 in *Changing Environments*, Heinemann 2000.

Quick check questions

1 Try to think of some more examples of positive influences that human activities have on the coastline.

2 Produce a conflict matrix for the contrasting activities on a stretch of coastline you are familiar with.

3 How might sea level changes affect coral reefs?

4 Compare the issues and management of coral reefs in Thailand with those in an example from a MEDC.

A review of management strategies

In this section you will be revising:

- **factors influencing decisions on coastal management**
- **concepts of environmental impact, cost-benefit analysis, integrated coastal management and sustainable management**
- **evaluation of a full spectrum of management strategies from hard engineering to 'do nothing' at locations along an extended stretch of coastline**

- **examples of contrasting policies and strategies from the UK and one other country**
- **case studies to examine reasons for increased demand for coastal management.**

Coastal management

Coastal management is wide-ranging and may focus on:

- reducing the impact of coastal processes
- reducing the impact of landform development on human activity
- protecting coastal ecosystems
- managing human use of, or pressure on, the coastal zone.

Reasons for possible increased demand for coastal management:

- rising sea levels associated with global warming
- more frequent storm activity
- continuing coastal development.

Factors in deciding what management strategy should be undertaken include:

- technical: whether it will solve the problem
- economic: the cost/benefit assessment of the scheme
- environmental: what impacts the scheme will have on the environments and knock-on effects further down the coast
- political: how it is seen by people in the local area, region, country or internationally
- whether anything needs to be done at all, depending on the value of what is being protected
- sustainability: whether it will have knock-on effects that affect resources for future generations.

Hard and soft engineering. Hard engineering options can also be sub-divided into those that operate on the cliff face (to reduce sub-aerial and mass movement processes) and those that focus on the foot of the cliff to reduce wave energy or to protect the base of the cliff or beach from erosion by the sea (Table 1, page 66).

Beach management strategies are used in areas without a cliff or as a cliff foot strategy. These methods aim to increase the size of the beach store by artificial means or by working with natural processes (Table 2, page 66).

Shoreline management plans (SMPs) offer a more integrated management approach by examining the processes and possible solutions within sediment sub-cells. SMPs usually follow certain stages.

1   Collect and analyse data on the coastal processes, the current management situation, existing land use and any planned coastal developments.

2   Set clear objectives and consult expert opinion.
3   Consider various management methods in the light of the information gained at stage 1.
4   Publish a plan and allow comment from local businesses, residents and other people interested in that particular coastal area.

Reminder

Make sure that you learn the detail of a range of management strategies in MEDCs and LEDCs.

Hard engineering: overcoming natural processes			
Strategy	**Purpose**	**Strengths**	**Weaknesses**
(1) Cliff-foot strategies, to protect the cliff foot or beach from soil erosion:			
Sea walls: **Recurved sea wall**	Massive, made of concrete; increasingly used to reflect rather than prevent waves	Traditional solution to protect valuable or high-risk property, dense population or resources	Expensive (£1m per km); may stop sediment going elsewhere if sea walls reflect rather than absorb wave energy (depends on design); foundations can be undermined by scour
Revetments: **Wooden revetment** Open structure of planks to absorb wave energy but allowing water and sediment to build up beyond.	Massive, made of rocks, concrete or wood; absorb wave energy; porous; act as baffles	As sea walls, but relatively cheaper	When resting on sand and shingle, can be undermined and moved by storm waves; environmentally ugly
Gabions: Steel mesh cage filled with small rocks	Smaller rocks held in wire cages	Have some properties of both sea walls and revetments, yet much cheaper; small rocks help to absorb wave energy and reduce erosion	Relatively lightweight and small-scale solution; environmentally ugly
Groynes	Hold beach material carried along by longshore drift	Low initial cost and repaired easily	May starve downdrift areas of sand and shingle, and therefore increase erosion in these areas
Offshore breakwaters	Reduce power of waves offshore	Can be built from waste material or create artificial reefs	Possible ecological impacts and may not work on a large scale
Rip-rap (rock armour)	Large rocks at foot of sea walls or cliffs to absorb waves	Effective, cheaper than revetments, prevent undermining	May move in very heavy storm conditions
(2) Cliff-face strategies, to reduce damage to cliff face from sub-aerial erosion:			
Cliff drainage	Removal of water from rock prevents landslide or slumping	Cost-effective	Drains can become new weaknesses; dry cliffs can cause rock falls
Cliff regarding	Low angle of cliffs to prevent collapse	Works on clay material, when little else will	Retreat of cliff line uses up large areas of land

Table 1 Management strategies: hard options

Soft engineering: working with natural processes			
Strategy	**Purpose**	**Strengths**	**Weaknesses**
Offshore reefs	Mining waste or old tyres fastened together and sunk; reduces wave energy as waves approach the shore	Relatively cost-effective and low technology; good use for waste material	Largely untested beyond research level and may have pollution implications
Beach nourishment	Sand pumped from seabed to replace eroded beach	Natural-looking result; useful in areas of recreation and tourism	Very expensive; may erode again or have ecological impacts
Managed retreat	New buildings and defences are prevented or existing structures dismantled; incentives given through grants etc.	Cost-effective; preserves natural coastline	Difficult to persuade people they are safe or that the local council are not 'abandoning their responsibilities'
'Do nothing'	Accept that there is no economically-viable or technically-feasible solution	Cost-effective; allows chance to research or await new technologies	Unpopular locally with political implications
Red-lining	Artificial line drawn on a map with planning permission withdrawn from the area within; new line of defence set up inland - 'set-back' schemes	Cost-effective	Unpopular locally; political implications

Table 2 Management strategies: soft options

An example of managed retreat, a more **sustainable** approach to coastal management, is shown in Figure 1.

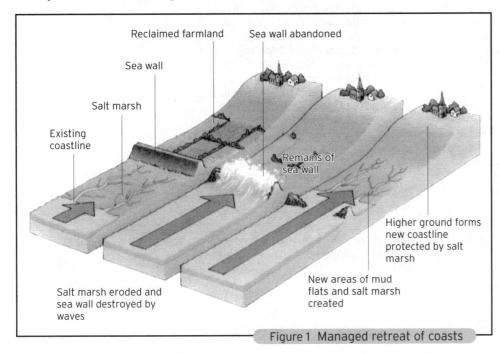

Figure 1 Managed retreat of coasts

Labels within figure:
- Reclaimed farmland
- Sea wall abandoned
- Sea wall
- Salt marsh
- Existing coastline
- Remains of sea wall
- Higher ground forms new coastline protected by salt marsh
- New areas of mud flats and salt marsh created
- Salt marsh eroded and sea wall destroyed by waves

Case studies of contrasting strategies

The Keta Sea Defence Project, West Africa

This was funded using $94m of overseas aid from the USA, EU funding and part of the 1999 government expenditure for Ghana. The project has four elements.

- A sea wall constructed at Keta to limit further erosion.
- Land reclamation of 300ha from the lagoon adjacent to the town of Keta, providing an area for local inhabitants to re-build homes that were lost to erosion.
- Construction of a 8.3km causeway at Keta Lagoon between Keta and Havedzi, re-establishing a road link between these townships that was lost due to erosion.
- Flood control for Keta Lagoon, providing relief from extreme flooding conditions for people living around the lagoon.

Bangladesh: an issue of coastal flooding

The impacts of the 1998 flood:

- Duration: 21 days; July–September.
- 57 per cent of the land area was flooded, including large areas of farmland.
- 1050 people were killed and millions made homeless.
- In Assam, more than one million people lost their homes.
- In Nalbari, 240 villages were submerged.
- At Sandwip, a large coastal island, an embankment was breached by the high tide stranding 1200 families.
- Floods also caused shortages in food and drinking water plus an increase in diseases such as diarrhoea and respiratory infections.
- Cost of the flood is estimated at $1billion.

(See also Table 3, page 67.)

Key concepts

Environmental impact looks at the range of impacts of a coastal development project. It is usually carried out where there is a risk that natural ecosystems will be affected.

Integrated coastal management is the joining together of various elements to form a comprehensive attempt at solving the problems along a stretch of coastline.

Sustainable management schemes are schemes that meet the needs of the present without compromising the ability of future generations to meet their own needs. Key aspects of such schemes value the environment, attempt to preserve people's livelihoods, do not commit local authorities to a future of costly repairs, and involve local people in the decision-making process.

Reminder

For details on the issues and management of the Northumberland coast, see pages 96–115 in *Changing Environments*, Heinemann 2000.

Physical causes	Human causes
● Most of the country consists of the large floodplains and delta of the Ganges and Brahmaputra rivers	● Deforestation has occurred in the areas of the rivers' headwaters in Nepal and Tibet to provide fuel, timber and grazing land for an increasing population. Removal of trees reduces interception and increases overland flow, soil erosion and landslides, increasing the river bed by 5cm per year
● 70 per cent of the area is <1m above sea level	
● Rivers, lakes and marshland cover 10 per cent of the land area	
● Tropical cyclones bring heavy rain and storm waves cause coastal floods	● The building of the Farraka Dam in 1971 reduced the discharge of the river during the dry season which encourages sedimentation on the river bed and so increases the risk of flooding
● Snowmelt from the glaciers in the Himalayas in late spring and summer increases discharges	
● There are heavy monsoon rains especially over the Himalayas, the uplands in Assam and the Central Indian Plateau	● Urbanisation and the development of roads and embankments hinder the free drainage of water from the land
● One theory suggests that increased global temperatures and sea levels, due to global warming, causes increased rainfall in the Himalayas	

Table 3 Causes of flooding

Management schemes

● A master plan of hard engineering schemes including embankments, dredging, river diversion, meander cut-offs and by-pass channels was devised (Figure 2). For example, the Meghna-Dhonagoda Irrigation Project, built between 1964 and 1970 at a cost of $50m, consisted of embankments to enclose an area of 200km^2 crossed by irrigation channels. This was then reinforced in the 1980s by a second set of embankments, three km away from the original ones.

● An action plan for flood control was instituted, which involved 3500km of embankments and included compartments for floodwater storage that allowed controlled flooding to take place. River training was also part of this scheme and attempts to divert river flow in such a way as to minimise bank erosion and scouring. The first phase was completed between 1990 and 1995 and cost $150m, aided by international and NGO funding.

● By 2005, a range of projects will be undertaken, costing around $500m. These will focus on the construction of new embankments in the upper sections of the main rivers. This construction will gradually be extended downstream in stages, allowing river channels to adjust to increased flood flow and sediment load from the sections upstream. As embankments are completed, compartments will be created behind them. However, 'normal' levels of floodwater will be allowed to maintain rice farming in the surrounding area.

● Improved flood forecasting.

● Better disaster preparation, including provision of boats for escape and shelters on raised ground.

Reminder

For more detail on flooding and management schemes in Bangladesh, see pages 144–157 in *Changing Environments*, Heinemann 2000.

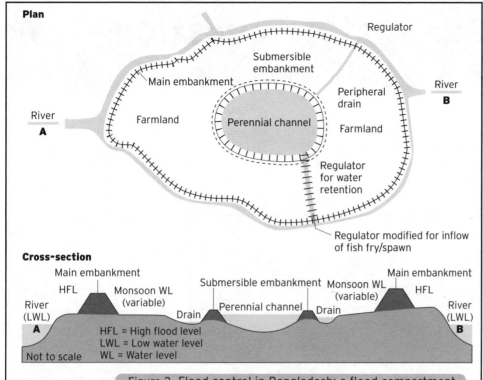

Figure 2 Flood control in Bangladesh: a flood compartment

Remaining issues

- If flooding does occur, embankments may make this worse.
- There is a problem of erosion of the embankments because of their construction so close to the river.
- Embankments speed up river flow, increasing discharge and sediment downstream, causing further problems.
- There is lack of involvement or consultation of the local population.
- Fish migration and breeding is inhibited.

 Quick check questions

1 For a management example you have studied, identify what factors have been important in deciding whether to go ahead with the scheme.

2 Outline the process of managed retreat in Figure 1.

3 Identify the different types of management used on a coastline you have studied. Which are hard engineering solutions and which are soft engineering options?

4 Compare the approaches to coastal management used in two of the examples outlined here, or compare one with another you have studied. Outline why there are similarities/differences.

1. Study the sketch below (Figure 1) which shows a short stretch of coastline.
   i) Name the three coastal features at A, B and C. (3)
   ii) Compare the profile of the cliffs at A with that behind B, and give reasons for the differences. (6)
   iii) Suggest the possible effects on this coast if the groynes were removed. (3)

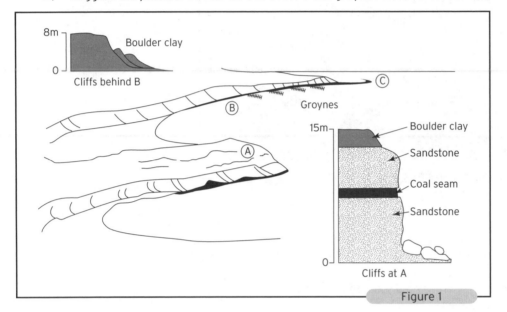

Figure 1

2. Explain how the coastline could be considered an open system. (5)

3. Suggest what short-term and long-term responses decision-makers might make to reduce the risk of coastal flooding. (5)

4. Study Figure 2 which shows the integrated coastal protection scheme at Sidmouth, Devon.

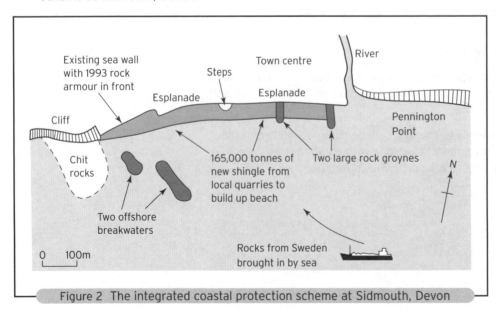

Figure 2 The integrated coastal protection scheme at Sidmouth, Devon

i)   Explain how the various elements of the scheme shown work
together to protect Sidmouth.   (5)

ii) Since the development of this scheme, two issues have emerged:
- erosion is increasing at Pennington Point
- coastal defences may be affecting tourism.

Suggest why each has become an issue.   (6)

5. State three conditions which are necessary for sand dunes to form
along coasts.   (3)

6. Using a named example, outline how plant succession operates in a
sand dune ecosystem.   (6)

7. Study Figure 3 which illustrate three methods of hard engineering.

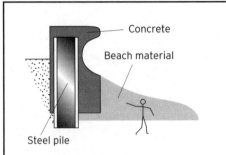

Large boulders dumped on beach

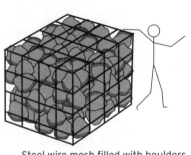

Steel wire mesh filled with boulders

Figure 3 Examples of hard engineering coastal defences

i)   Name each of the strategies.   (3)
ii) Examine their effectiveness in protecting the coastline.   (9)

8. Referring to a located stretch of coastline, examine the ways in which
human activities may lead to conflicts.   (10)

9. With reference to named examples, explain why successful management
of the coastline requires an understanding of coastal processes. (10)

10. Examine the possible impacts of global warming on the coastal
environments of named countries.   (10)

PART 2

Managing change in human environments

This module covers the *Managing change in human environments* element of the AS Specification that makes up the 6472 exam. Examples and case studies are included at relevant points. The two topics within this unit are Urban environments and Rural environments:

Urban environments

- Defining an urban area based on employment, population density and functions
- The concept of urbanisation and the urbanisation cycle
- How the nature and importance of urban environments vary spatially, including the concept of millionaire, mega and world cities
- Issues of sustainability in rapidly growing cities
- Spatial development of land use within an urban area and factors affecting this with reference to land use zoning and urban models
- Concept of centrifugal forces and centripetal forces and the resultant change in the Central Business District (CBD) and rural-urban fringe; issues of people, employment and services and possible conflict or competition that may arise
- The use of regeneration/re-imaging to get people back to the inner cities of MEDCs
- How quality of life varies within urban environments in MEDCs and LEDCs
- The concept of urban deprivation and the cycle of deprivation
- The challenges of managing urban environments and examining how successful planners and decision makers have been in managing change and conflict with reference to the options on managing environmental problems in the city and managing housing stock
- The possible future of urban areas with a more sustainable approach to planning, including managing the Brown Agenda in LEDC cities.

Rural environments

- The problems of defining the boundary between a rural area and an urban one; the rural-urban continuum and the definition of rurality
- Perceptions of rural and urban living
- The changing relationships between rural and urban area development
- How and why rural environments vary in landscape and character; looking at physical, socio-economic and cultural factors in more economically developed countries (MEDCs) and less economically developed countries (LEDCs)
- Socio-economic processes that have led to change and modification of rural environments and communities, such as changing farming methods or the diversification into tourism
- The effect of changes in population, (decline and expansion), in MEDC and LEDC rural areas and possible conflicts that may emerge
- The challenges of managing rural environments and examining how successful planners and decision makers have been in managing change and conflict with reference to the options on managing the countryside for recreation and tourist use and managing rural deprivation and rural poverty
- The possible future of rural areas with the alternative approach of more innovative or sustainable development strategies.

More detail on what you need to know for each of these elements is given at the beginning of each of the sections.

In this section, you will be revising:

- what characteristics make an urban area
- a definition of urbanisation
- reasons for urbanisation: demographic, migratory and economic

- the cycle of urbanisation applied to a range of countries at different stages of development and changes over time.

What does 'urban' mean?

Urban settlements can be defined:

- by population size, density of housing or number of dwellings. For example:
  Sweden = 200 people   India = 386 people/sq km
  Netherlands = 20,000   Peru: town = > 100 dwellings
- by employment: a large percentage of the working population engaged in manufacturing or office activities. For example, in the Netherlands, urban areas have <20 per cent in farming
- by facilities and functions: urban areas usually have high level of services (piped water, sewerage, medical and retail facilities)
- by government legislation. For example, in Pakistan, a town has a town committee; in the UK, a city has a cathedral.

Urbanisation

The main phase of **urbanisation** in MEDCs occurred in the nineteenth century, associated with industrialisation and economic development. In LEDCs, it has occurred post-1950 associated with rural to urban migration (largely due to rural change), and natural increase (due to falling death rates).

The main reasons for urbanisation are:

- the movement of people (migration) from rural to urban areas, which exceeds the migration of residents from urban to rural areas
- urban areas often have better access to medical and other services than rural areas do, which results in a greater life expectancy in urban areas than in rural ones; this, in turn, may attract even more migrants
- natural population increase (the difference between birth rate and death rate) is greater in urban than in rural areas, so the urban population grows more rapidly.

Urbanisation has resulted in a change in the proportion of urban and rural residents in the world's population. The urbanisation/ruralisation graphs (Figure 1) show the change in percentage urban or percentage rural population with economic development over time. The typical graph follows a S-shaped curve. In many developed countries, the level of urbanisation has stabilised at 80 per cent of the total population.

The urbanisation curve is largely based on MEDCs. It is assumed that LEDCs will follow the same sequence but not necessarily at the same pace (see Figure 1).

Reminder

Look at a variety of photographs of urban areas, in LEDCs as well as MEDCs. Consider what factors have affected how the scene looks.

Key concepts

Urbanisation is the process whereby an increasing proportion of the population of the world, a country, or a region live in urban areas.

Suburbanisation: the movement of people, factories, offices and shops out of the central area of cities and into the suburbs.

Counterurbanisation: the movement of people away from towns and cities to live in villages and small towns in the countryside.

Re-urbanisation: the movement of people back into the central area of a city after it has experienced a period of decline. Some form of city centre redevelopment is often the catalyst that starts this process.

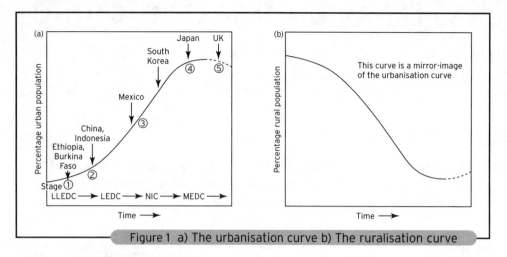

Figure 1 a) The urbanisation curve b) The ruralisation curve

The cycle of urbanisation

There are at least five stages in the process of urbanisation (Table 1).

Stages in urbanisation	Application to the UK	Approximate date
1 Very slow growth with most people employed in agriculture (rural society phase)	Primarily agricultural/craft economy	Pre 1750s– late 18th century
2 Increase in rate of urbanisation associated with economic development (take-off phase)	Urbanisation with economic development alongside the Industrial Revolution	Early 19th century 1750s–1830s
3 Rapid rise in urbanisation	3 a) Rapid urbanisation with industrial growth; migration from rural to urban areas	Nineteenth century
	b) **Surburbanisation**: suburbs grow faster than the central areas; the city grows outwards	1920s onwards
4 Urbanisation slows considerably; the majority of people live in towns and cities and are employed in industry and services	4 The suburbs continue to attract people but inner city population declines. Development of peripheral industrial estates and retail areas	1950s–1970s
5 **Counterurbanisation** occurs and the urban proportion stabilises or decreases as some people prefer to commute	5 People move to adjacent rural areas or to smaller towns further away	1970s onwards
6 **Re-urbanisation** associated with urban renewal	6 Some movement back to the centre due to gentrification, redevelopment and/or the creation of job opportunities in the central area	Late 1980s onwards

Table 1 The urbanisation cycle

Urbanisation is often accompanied by other changes.

- A shift in the economy with the emphasis moving from farming (primary sector) to manufacturing and more centralised services.
- The concentration of people and their non-agricultural activities at favoured locations.
- The spread of urbanism, that is a change in lifestyle, values, behaviour and social institutions.
- Some settlements at favoured locations grow more quickly than others to become towns, some towns grow into cities, and so on.

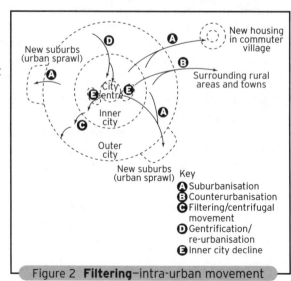

Figure 2 **Filtering**—intra-urban movement

Quick check questions

1 How does economic development appear to affect urbanisation?

2 Give reasons why the UK has experienced very slow rates of urbanisation over the last 50 years.

Millionaire, mega and world cities

In this section, you will be revising:

- definitions of millionaire, mega and world cities
- awareness of the changing pattern of millionaire / mega cities

- issues of sustainability of rapidly-growing cities.

Settlement size

Table 1 shows a classification of settlements in the UK, based on size.

Settlement	Population
Hamlet	< 250
Village	250–2000
Small town	2001–10,000
Large town	10,001–100,000
City	100,001–1,000,000
Millionaire city	A city with at least 1,000,000 people
Super city	5,000,000 or more
Mega city	10,000,000 or more

Table 1 Classification of settlements in the UK

A **world city** is a very large city, which is important within the world economy and not just within the economy of one country. Examples of world cities include London, New York and Paris.

Spatial distribution

In 1950, only New York and London were defined as mega cities. By 1990, there were twenty mega cities, fourteen in LEDCs (Figure 1). Today there are around 25 mega-cities; nineteen in LEDCs. Other trends can be seen when looking at continental patterns.

Key concepts

Urban hierarchy: a system of urban centres in a region or country based on size and function which range from the smallest to the largest, and from the least specialised to the most specialised.

Conurbation: a large urban area formed by the expansion of one major centre or the coalescing of several smaller urban centres.

Megalopolis: a very large urban area developed by the merging of several cities, for example, Trenton, Newark, Jersey City, Paterson, New York along the north-east coast of the USA.

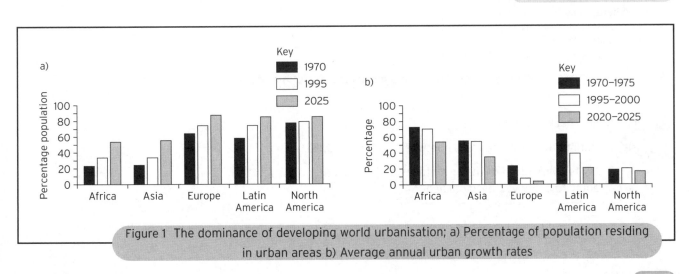

Figure 1 The dominance of developing world urbanisation; a) Percentage of population residing in urban areas b) Average annual urban growth rates

Urban growth

The growth of urban areas is due to both **push** and **pull factors**.

Mega cities have developed due to:

- historically-important sites; for example, Shanghai, China was a colonial trading port
- spearheaded industrialisation as LEDCs develop into NICs, for example, São Paulo
- very favourable site and situation factors which give cultural, political and economic importance and produces **primate cities**, for example, Bangkok
- rapid population growth in certain LEDC cities due to a combination of a young population and rapid rural-urban migration
- cities in economic core areas which have high levels of education, technology and service provision and therefore become hosts to international investment.

However, there are disadvantages to mega cities, as well as advantages (see Table 2).

Key concepts

Pull factors: these factors attract rural population to urban areas, e.g. better health care and more jobs.
Push factors: these factors encourage rural populations to leave the area, e.g. natural disasters such as drought.
Primate city: a city that dominates a country's urban system, with a population more than twice that of the second largest city.

Advantages	Disadvantages/issues of the rapid growth of cities
More productive economy allows a concentration of industry and finance and provides a ready market and available pool of labour	A mega city (and often the primary city) becomes a magnet for immigration. This becomes a problem when the rate of inward movement is faster than economic and infrastructure development
Provision of services and facilities such as education, piped water, electricity, healthcare, is often better than in rural areas	Acute environmental problems often develop such as air and water pollution from factories and a rapid increase in cars and congestion; problems of waste and sewage disposal is also an issue in some cities
Particular initiatives improve literacy or women's health especially in informal areas	The informal employment sector rarely receives support from government and is often a target for harassment
Strong local government that promotes companies to move to the outskirts of the city as well as the established areas, strengthens the wider region surrounding the city, e.g. Buenos Aires	Spontaneous housing which spreads rapidly and is uncontrolled provides problems for urban planning and redevelopment as well as increasing the risk of hazards such as landslides or flood damage
Emergence of the informal employment sector allows entrepreneurial talent and the creation of social networks within shanty areas	Key services such as hospitals and universities are often in the wealthy parts of the city. This reinforces the divide in the quality of life between the higher-paid social elite and people in the lower-paid manual or informal sectors
Self-help housing allows homes to be built at a rate that money and family circumstances allow	Urban sprawl accentuates transport problems.
Large cities are a focus for investment both internationally and nationally which leads to modernisation and an increase in personal wealth	
Work in the urban formal sector is often better paid than farming	
The provision of commercial opportunities for farmers close to the city encourages more intensive farming	

Table 2 Advantages and disadvantages of mega cities

 Quick check questions

1 Outline the changing trends between 1970 and 2025.

2 Try to think which of the advantages and disadvantages in Table 1 apply to a city you have studied.

In this section, you will be revising:

- **factors affecting spatial development of land use in an urban area**
- **the bid rent theory**

- **urban models for MEDCs and LEDCs, such as Mann's model**

The bid rent theory

Functions within urban areas are usually arranged into distinct land use zones. An example is the Central Business District (CBD). One of the main reasons for this zoning is the cost of land within the urban area. This is reflected by the **bid rent theory** (see Figure 1).

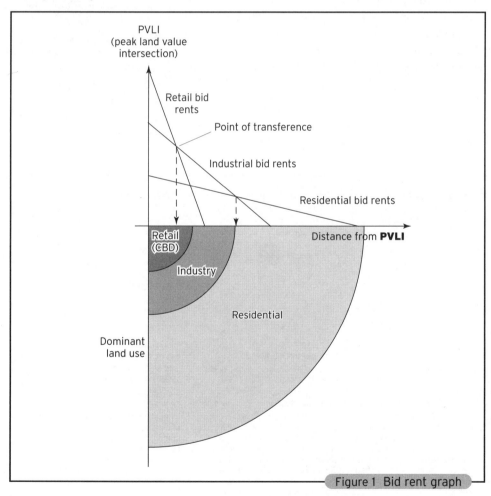

Figure 1 Bid rent graph

Key concepts

Bid rent theory: a model which tries to explain urban structure in terms of the profitability of land which, in turn, reflects accessibility. It is based on the highest bidder being willing to pay rent because they are likely to make the most profit from setting up on that piece of land.
Peak land value intersection (PLVI): the point in an urban area, usually in the CBD, that commands the highest rent/price per square metre.

Reminder

It is the point or margin of transference (that is, the point where the curves for competing land uses intersect) which determines the change from one land use to another, not the point where the bid rent is zero.

When major roads intersect, for example, where ring roads meet main roads that lead out of a city, secondary peaks in bid rent may develop (Figure 2, page 78). These are also likely to coincide with the development of suburban shopping centres or industrial estates.

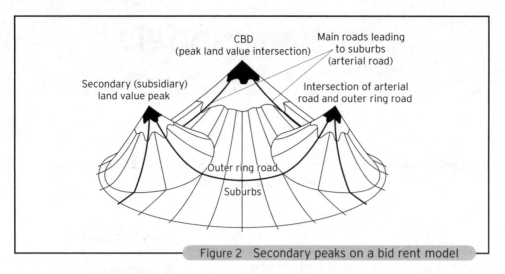

Figure 2 Secondary peaks on a bid rent model

Criticisms of the model are that:

- the model fails to take account of inherited land uses, topography, urban planning and subjective reasons for buyers wanting a particular site
- it assumes that the CBD is the point of maximum accessibility and the place where most people will have employment. In fact, employment has often moved to suburban locations rather than in the traditional zone close to the CBD
- it assumes that each piece of land will be used in the most profitable way.

Land use models

Several attempts have been made to summarise general patterns of land use in MEDCs into models (see Figure 3).

Reminder

The Mann model is specifically identified in the specifications and it is based on UK cities, so that might be a good one to learn. However, depending on the wording of the exam question, it might be appropriate to use others instead.

---

a The concentric model

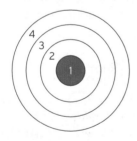

b The sector model

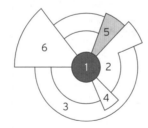

c The multiple-nuclei model

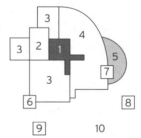

d Mann's model

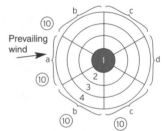

Concentric model

Devised by: Ernest W. Burgess, 1920s, Chicago USA

Main processes: centrality and mobility

Offices and businesses are located in the central business district (CBD) around which is a zone in transition, where commercial, industrial and low-income residential uses are mixed. Residential zones are arranged in concentric circles of increasing affluence with distance from the centre. Wealthier families, who can afford to travel, live in the commuter suburbs where they can buy more land for larger houses/gardens. Poorer families and individuals live nearer the centre, in smaller flats or houses.

Sector model

Devised by: Homer Hoyt, 1930s, USA

Main processes: accessibility, proximity and centrality

Radial transport routes from the CBD to the suburbs give rise to sectors. High-income sectors avoid industry and low-income areas. Local geographical factors such as hills or rivers mean that cities often develop more in certain directions than others.

Multiple-nuclei model

Devised by: Chauncey Harris and Edward Ullman, 1940s, USA

Main processes: centrality, clustering and proximity

Cities tend to grow from more than one centre or nucleus at a time. Each centre has a different function or purpose. When old nuclei are congested, new ones develop. Similar land uses tend to cluster together. Certain land uses, e.g. industry, repel others, such as high-quality housing.

Mann's model

Devised by: P Mann, 1965, based on UK cities

Main processes: centrality, clustering and mobility

Concentric zones based on the age of development reflect the outwards spread of the city. Superimposed on this pattern are sectors based on social class. The key factor is the prevailing westerly wind in the UK which at the time of centrally-located heavy industry would blow smoke eastwards across the city. High-class residential would locate upwind of this industry to the west. Low-class residential would have no choice but to develop close to the factories, (due to land cost and proximity to work).

Key

■ CBD	4 or b Medium-class residential	7 Outlying business district	10 Commuter zone/commuter villages
2 Wholesale light manufacturing	5 or a High-class residential	8 Residential suburb	
3 or c Low-class residential	6 or d Heavy manufacturing	9 Industrial suburb	

Figure 3 Models of urban land use

According to these theoretical models, certain key factors influence land use in an urban area:

- accessibility and communications networks
- market forces
- the ability to pay for a desired site, (i.e. the bid rent theory).

However, such models do not always reflect other factors or developments that are important today such as:

- topography
- changing industry (from manufacturing to more service and light industry), and its location (from a central area towards a location on the edge of the urban area)
- migration to smaller towns and villages (suburbanisation)
- city centre change; either decline or redevelopment
- **gentrification** of the inner city
- incentives to develop in certain areas, such as EU funding
- urban planning regulations which control where developments can take place
- Internet and tele-working, which have already affected the distribution of workplaces.

Land use patterns in typical LEDC cities are somewhat different. Look at the land use model of a Latin American city (Figure 4).

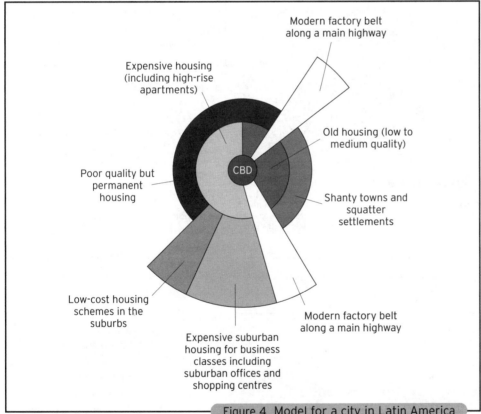

Figure 4 Model for a city in Latin America

Key concepts

Urban morphology: the form or shape of a town and the arrangement and layout of its buildings.

Zone in transition: the area around the CBD which is a mixed land use zone including car parks, derelict buildings, older housing, industrial buildings, (some of which may have been converted into housing).

Gentrification: a process in which run-down houses in inner city or other neglected areas are improved by relatively affluent people who move there in order to have easier access to the jobs and services of the city centre.

Functional zoning: the division of an area in a city into separate zones in which the businesses perform similar functions, e.g. a financial district such as the City of London, or the jewellery quarter in Birmingham.

Agglomeration: when businesses benefit from locating together within a particular area, for example, car showrooms or estate agents.

Quick check questions

1 At what point does the model (Figure 2) suggest that land use will change from retail to industrial?

2 Consider how the land use models fit with the land use pattern in a MEDC urban area and in a LEDC urban area that you have studied. Also think about what key factors affect these land use patterns

The changing Central Business District

In this section, you will be revising:

- the characteristics of a Central Business District (CBD)
- the core frame model
- zones of assimilation and discard

- the impact of out-of-town developments
- ways of re-generating and re-imaging the CBD
- examples of changing CBDs.

Characteristics of the CBD

The Central Business District is the centre of a city's commercial, social and cultural activities. The area has a number of clear characteristics (Figure 1).

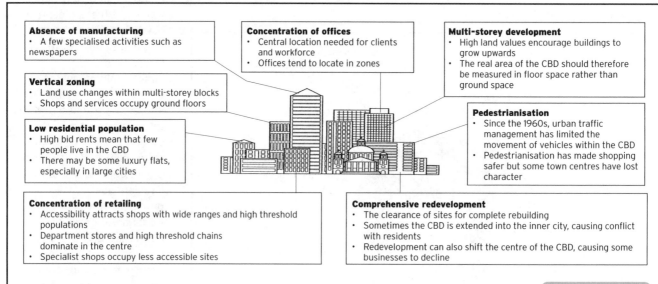

Absence of manufacturing
- A few specialised activities such as newspapers

Vertical zoning
- Land use changes within multi-storey blocks
- Shops and services occupy ground floors

Low residential population
- High bid rents mean that few people live in the CBD
- There may be some luxury flats, especially in large cities

Concentration of offices
- Central location needed for clients and workforce
- Offices tend to locate in zones

Multi-storey development
- High land values encourage buildings to grow upwards
- The real area of the CBD should therefore be measured in floor space rather than ground space

Pedestrianisation
- Since the 1960s, urban traffic management has limited the movement of vehicles within the CBD
- Pedestrianisation has made shopping safer but some town centres have lost character

Concentration of retailing
- Accessibility attracts shops with wide ranges and high threshold populations
- Department stores and high threshold chains dominate in the centre
- Specialist shops occupy less accessible sites

Comprehensive redevelopment
- The clearance of sites for complete rebuilding
- Sometimes the CBD is extended into the inner city, causing conflict with residents
- Redevelopment can also shift the centre of the CBD, causing some businesses to decline

Figure 1 The CBD

The core frame model was suggested by Horwood and Boyce in 1959 (Figure 2) and looks at different areas that make up the CBD.

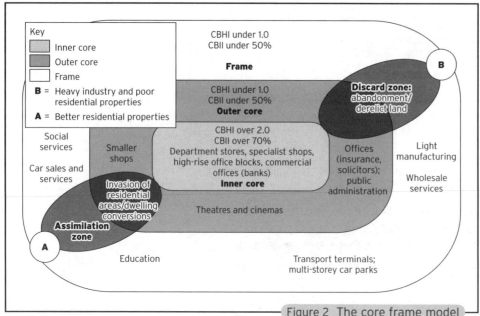

Key
- Inner core
- Outer core
- Frame
- **B** = Heavy industry and poor residential properties
- **A** = Better residential properties

CBHI under 1.0
CBII under 50%
Frame

CBHI under 1.0
CBII under 50%
Outer core

CBHI over 2.0
CBII over 70%
Department stores, specialist shops, high-rise office blocks, commercial offices (banks)
Inner core

Discard zone: abandonment/ derelict land

Social services

Car sales and services

Smaller shops

Invasion of residential areas/dwelling conversions

Assimilation zone

Theatres and cinemas

Offices (insurance, solicitors); public administration

Light manufacturing

Wholesale services

Education

Transport terminals; multi-storey car parks

Figure 2 The core frame model

Key concepts

Zone of assimilation: an area where the CBD is undergoing expansion due to a particular redevelopment scheme or flagship development.

Zone of discard: an area of the CBD which is in decline, perhaps due to a derelict site.

Flagship scheme: a high profile development, designed to encourage investment into an area and to be a model for further development.

The frame of the CBD is less intensively developed or visited and has lower land values and building heights. It has few or no parking restrictions and has more varied functions, but there are still some sub-zones or linkages such as car sales/services. It has some overlap with a zone-in-transition.

Centrifugal and centripetal forces

A large urban area has a complex structure and land use pattern, which reflects a balance between these two sets of influences: that is, it is in equilibrium (Figure 3).

Reminder

You may know **centripetal** and **centrifugal** forces as push and pull factors

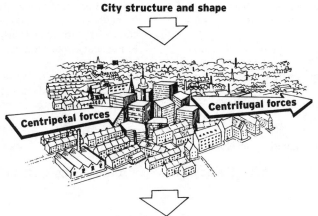

Factors which tend to **'pull'** or **attract** functions towards the centre of an urban area include:

A maximum accessibility

B maximum potential threshold population

C prestige derived from fashionable central address

D ability and opportunity for certain functions to cluster (e.g. finance, shops, entertainments)

E proximity of residence to range of entertainments

Factors which tend to **'push'** or **dispel** functions away from central urban areas to newly developing regions include:

A lack of space for expansion

B increasing land or bid rents

C congestion reducing efficiency of transport

D lack of suitable site for changing needs

E restrictions on development at city centre

F government incentive for ex-urban sites

City structure and shape

Urban evolution

Figure 3 Centrifugal and centripetal forces

Factors influencing CBD decline

- Rent, rates and/or land costs are high in the CBD, leading to an abandoned CBD or 'dead heart'.
- City centres are perceived to have poor infrastructure, to be ageing and dirty, and, in some cases, to be unsafe (Figure 4).
- A rise in car ownership has led to increased personal mobility.
- Congestion in **inner city** areas reduces the ease of accessibility to the CBD.

Key concept

Inner city: the part of the city centre that includes the CBD and a small area of land immediately surrounding it. In the UK this area has experienced much change since the 1970s such as road improvements, and urban renewal.

Some city centres have failed to compete with out-of-town developments and have declined
Decentralised services have produced growth and sprawl in the suburbs and edge cities

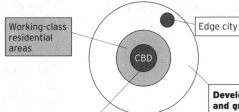

Working-class residential areas

Edge city

CBD

Development of suburbs and greenfield sites
- Wealthy and more affluent sectors move out
- Car-orientated shopping
- Pleasant atmosphere: large car parks, new large sites, accessible
- Lack of convenience for inner city population or public transport

Abandoned CBD or 'dead heart'
- Loss of multiple firms to out-of-town locations
- Erosion of trade and spiral decline
- Increasing unemployment
- Environmental decay: vacant buildings, vandalism and crime
- Depressing aging atmosphere
- Ghettos and slums form in the inner city and concentration of disadvantaged sectors
- Local authorities raise less money in business and household taxes which could lead to less direct investment

Figure 4 The 'urban doughnut' concept

- Companies are attracted to peripheral locations as they are cheaper; closer to affluent customers who live in the suburbs or outlying villages, have good accessibility and a better environment.
- Local planning policies sometimes encourage new industry to locate on new greenfield development locations to attract inward investment.

These factors also encourage out-of-town developments (see Table 1).

Advantages	Disadvantages
<ul><li>Relieves town centre traffic congestion</li><li>Provides large areas of on-site parking and easy accessibility for car users</li><li>Recent developments of transport termini have extended access to public transport for some centres, such as the Trafford Centre</li><li>Low land rents on the edge of the city keep prices low</li><li>One-stop, all-hours shopping is ideal for working families</li><li>Allows customers to choose goods from a large range of choice at cheaper prices</li><li>Out-of-town retail park shopping is now seem as a leisure activity</li><li>Clean functional buildings</li><li>May provide a focus for further suburban developments</li></ul>	<ul><li>Loss of greenbelt land</li><li>Causes serious localised traffic congestion</li><li>Companies control prices</li><li>Up to 25 per cent of the city's population, especially those in the inner city areas, do not have access to a car and connections to public transport routes are often complex</li><li>Stores and layout are often difficult to access for older or infirm users</li><li>No heritage; large barn-like structures with little 'character'</li><li>Blights the CBD and increases the dereliction of town centre streets, which may in turn cause other social problems</li></ul>

Table 1 The advantages and disadvantages of out-of-town retail development

Edge cities

There are over 150 edge cities in the USA and over 80 that are up-and-coming or planned. They have common characteristics:

- at least five million square feet of office space
- at least 600 000 square feet of retail space (the size of a large regional shopping centre)
- more jobs than bedrooms, i.e. they are not residential suburbs
- they are perceived as a single place and 'have it all' by local people
- they are nothing like a 'city' was 30 years ago
- they are linked to the broader metropolitan system by a transport and communication network.

Reviving the CBD

Various strategies have been used to regenerate the CBD and to encourage people to use this area again (Figure 5, page 83). Manchester is an example of a changing CBD and inner city area.

Reminder

Consider what factors have affected changes in a CBD that you have studied. Has the importance of each of these varied at different times in its development over the past 30 years?

Key concepts

Decentralisation: the movement of people, industry, shopping and office development away from city centres to the suburbs or peripheral out-of-town locations.

Edge cities: develop on the periphery of a large city and are socially and economically independent from the original core city.

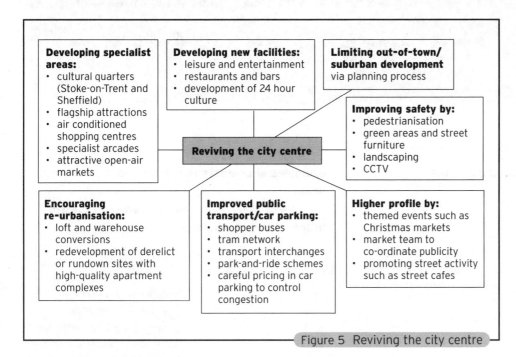

Figure 5 Reviving the city centre

Examples of Manchester's CBD initiatives

- New city centre housing: 2500 new dwellings (again partially funded by the CMDC). Most were warehouses converted into apartments.
- The Metrolink, a tram system was added to the transport network in 1992, bringing commuters and shoppers into the city centre from Bury in the north and Altrincham in the south.
- Redevelopment of the Arndale shopping centre in the CBD after the IRA bomb in 1996 destroyed a large part of the central area. This will also include a new transport interchange.
- Outdoor café area and new paving areas with sculptures in Ann's Square.
- **Flagship** development of a new Marks and Spencer store (the largest in the world when opened in 1999) and a new Selfridges store.
- Re-imaging of Exchange Square area in the Millennium Quarter district of the CBD including URBIS museum, bars, restaurants, street sculptures as well as Printworks, a US-style urban entertainment centre.
- Redevelopment of the bus station and adjacent Piccadilly Gardens to include new office development and multiple mini-water fountain features and seating.

Reminder

Look at Chapter 19 (pages 253–67) of *Changing Environments*, Heinemann 2000 for further details of Manchester's city centre.

Quick check questions

1 Outline some specific examples of the key characteristics and structure of a CBD that you have studied. How are these different in the core to those in the frame of this CBD?

2 How would the strategies in Figure 5 help to address the dead heart problem?

3 What characteristics do you think a successful regeneration scheme has?

Competition and conflicts in the rural–urban fringe

In this section, you will be revising:

- **examples of changes taking place at the rural-urban fringe**
- **the definition of sprawl**

- **examples of conflicts that have occurred in such areas**
- **the role of greenbelts and new towns to control urban fringe developments.**

The rural–urban fringe is very much an area in transition along the rural-urban continuum. However, issues in this area are different in MEDCs to LEDCs. The typical MEDC rural–urban fringe has seen many changes (see Figure 1).

Key concept

Negative externality: an unpleasant impact on people living in a particular area. For example, fumes from a factory or noise from an airport.

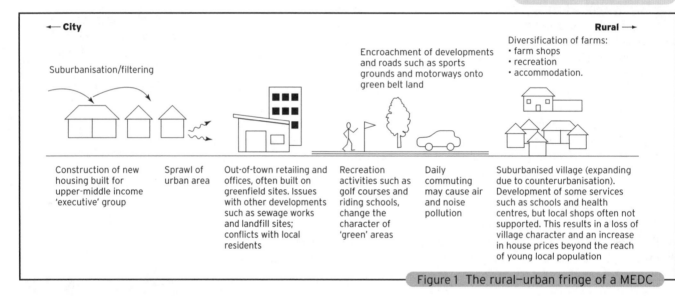

Figure 1 The rural–urban fringe of a MEDC

The typical LEDC rural–urban fringe has seen different changes (see Figure 2).

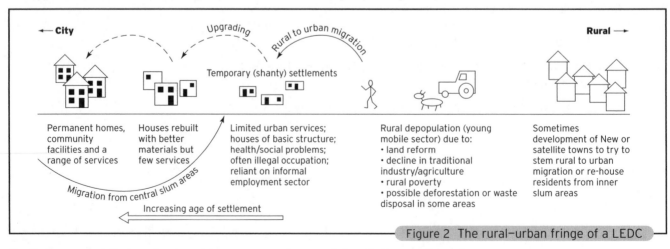

Figure 2 The rural–urban fringe of a LEDC

Conflict occurs at the rural–urban fringes over environmental, pollution, social and congestion issues.

Managing the rural–urban fringe

Greenbelts were first introduced in 1955 in order to:

- check **urban sprawl** (UK greenbelts total 4.5 million hectares)
- protect the countryside (greenbelts represent 35 per cent of the UK countryside)
- prevent neighbouring towns from merging into conurbations
- preserve historic towns
- assist in urban regeneration by focusing development within the urban boundaries.

It is not impossible to build on greenbelt land. Permission can be given for 'suitable use' or if a sufficiently good case is made. Threats to greenbelt land include:

- pressures for new housing, for example, increased demand in the South East
- major development projects, for example, the Channel Tunnel Rail Link
- major road schemes, for example, the M25
- changes in farming, for example, more recreation facilities, set-a-side, farm shops
- changes in government policy, for example, targets for new housing
- neglect, for example, tipping, dereliction.

The side effects of greenbelts include:

- Development is pushed out into the countryside, so called 'leap-frogging'.
- There is increased commuting through greenbelt areas which may produce more pollution and traffic noise in the greenbelt area.
- Less industrial development, which may result in companies moving elsewhere.
- Development is pushed into the city causing overcrowding and congestion.
- There are higher property prices within the city area due to restricted supply.

There is currently a debate about whether new development should be developed on **greenfield sites** on the edge of an urban area or on **brownfield sites** (Table 1).

Reasons for building on greenfield sites	Reasons for building on brownfield sites
- Quality of life is higher in rural areas - If all new housing was built on greenfield sites, 87 per cent of the UK's countryside would still remain un-urbanised - Restrictions on developing greenfield sites would make city housing more expensive, especially for the less well-off who would remain - Such sites do not have high clean up costs - Parts of the UK where most derelict land is located are not where the demand for new housing is greatest	- There are many brownfield sites available in urban areas - Would help regenerate inner city areas and reduce car dependency and urban sprawl - Government guidelines; e.g. '60 per cent of all new homes in the South East should be provided on brownfield sites' - Opposition from rural communities who fear that new house building on greenfield sites will alter the character of rural villages - Government figures for housing needs are disputed and may not be as high as first predicted

Table 1 Greenfield versus brownfield

New towns

Decentralisation and **new towns** are another way to tackle urban sprawl. New towns were designed to have:

- a population of 30,000 to 50,000 (towns in the second phase were larger)
- self-contained settlements
- neighbourhoods of mixed social classes
- new services such as schools, hospitals and shopping centres
- areas of planned open space
- industry largely separate from residential land use
- improved environment to attract investment and new companies
- a planned and integrated public transport network.
- re-housing residents from slum clearances in the inner city areas.

Reminder

Learn the detail of changes and issues in one named rural–urban fringe area.

Key concepts

Brownfield site a site that has been used previously for factories and/or housing. These buildings have now been demolished and cleared ready for redevelopment.
Greenbelt: an area around a city composed mostly of parkland and farmland, in which development is strictly controlled. Its purpose is to prevent two or more towns or cities from merging together to form one large urban area. An example is the greenbelt around London.
Greenfield site: an area, usually on the edge of a city, that has not been developed for housing, industry or transport. The area may still be farmland.
New town: a planned urban centre, designed to be freestanding, self-contained and socially balanced.
Urban sprawl: an increase in the area covered by urban activities. This is usually in the form of uncontrolled expansion in the outer fringe area of a city.

New towns have also been used in LEDCs to try to control **urban growth** and the expansion of shanty towns, as administrative centres such as Brasilia in Brazil, and even as a status symbol. For example, the Tenth Ramadan New Town was developed to help disperse some of Cairo's population in Egypt.

Problems with new towns, include: lack of maturity, being overplanned and too functional, and a lack of sufficient jobs for migrants. The centre of trade and culture remains in the 'old' city.

Case study of a new town: the Tenth Ramadan New Town

The Tenth Ramadan New Town, 55km away from Cairo in Egypt, was developed as part of a range of projects to disperse some of Cairo's population.

Sucesses	Problems
○ Aimed to house 300,000 people in six neighbourhood units ○ Each neighbourhood unit has a mixture of high-rise apartment blocks, some open space and gardens, a mosque, a junior school and a local shopping centre ○ Industrial zones separated from housing areas ○ Adjacent to major highways for accessibility	○ The scheme initially had great difficulty in attracting inhabitants and only had 30,000 after eight years ○ Many of the apartments were too expensive for the intended residents ○ Despite government help, new industries were slow to move into the New Town, which proved a disincentive for people to leave Cairo ○ Costs of travelling to Cairo for work, because of the lack of sufficient job opportunities in the new town, were prohibitive

Table 2 An analysis of the Tenth Ramadan New Town

 Quick check questions

1 Compare the changes that have occurred in rural–urban fringe areas in a typical MEDC with that in a LEDC.

2 For a greenbelt area you have studied, outline how pressures on this land have been managed.

3 Outline the successes and problems with the development of a new town you have studied in a MEDC.

Quality of life

In this section, you will be revising:

- **indicators that make up an assessment of the quality of life and/or deprivation**
- **awareness of the location and problems of 'poor' areas in MEDC and LEDC cities**

- **the cycle of urban deprivation**
- **knowledge of at least one LEDC city and one MEDC city.**

All cities contain inequality. In any city there is a complex set of reasons why wealthy and poor areas are found in particular locations. However, the key reasons are housing types, tenure and the socio-economic groups living in a particular area which are indicators of quality of life (QOL) (see Table 1).

Category	Definition	Examples of indicators
Economic	Inequality in the ownership of wealth or income	• Percentage owner-occupied housing • Percentage of population relying on state benefits
Social	Inequality in lifestyle or opportunity	• Percentage of the population suffering poor health • Percentage of population aged over 16 in full time education
Environmental	Inequality in the environmental quality of residential areas	• Incidence of litter, graffiti and vandalism • Levels of atmospheric pollution
Political	Inequality in access to decision-making processes	• Percentage of the electorate voting in local elections • Percentage of population participating in the local community (e.g. being a school governor or other volunteer work)

Table 1 QOL indicators

For a comparison of Quality of factors between an MEDC and an LEDC, see Figures 1 and 2 (page 88).

The top twelve features of cities that affect **quality of life** are:

1 Crime levels
2 Cost of living
3 Job prospects
4 Health services
5 Shopping facilities
6 Wage levels
7 Levels of unemployment
8 Quality of schools
9 Access to public housing
10 Cost of private housing
11 Sports and leisure facilities
12 Pollution

Key concepts

Standard of living: a household's level of income and their ability to pay for consumer goods, housing, leisure and services.

Quality of life (QOL): includes the quality of the environment in which people live as well as their standard of living.

Social segregation: the spatial or geographical separation of different social groups (i.e. wealthy groups live in a different area from poor groups).

Ghetto: an urban district containing a high proportion of one particular ethnic group. The word comes from the district of Geto in medieval Venice which was reserved for Jews.

QoL profiles for typical MEDC and LEDC cities

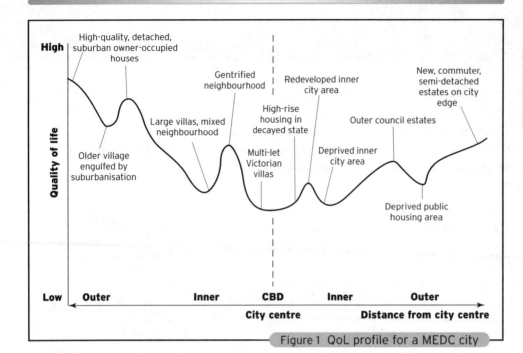

Figure 1 QoL profile for a MEDC city

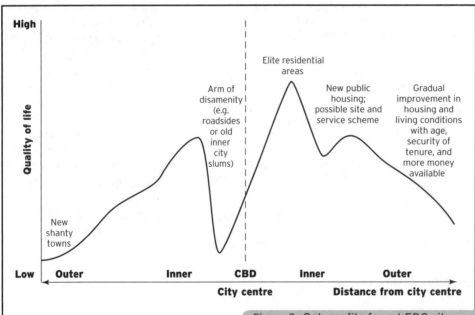

Figure 2 QoL profile for a LEDC city

There can be other consequences of inequality such as social disorder and perhaps increased crime levels, as well as the issue of declining environmental conditions and health in poorer areas that all lead to a cycle of the deprivation (see Figure 3).

Key concepts

Deprivation: a deprived area is one in which the population has a quality of life which is below the minimum regarded as acceptable by a particular society at a particular time.
Multiple deprivation: a neighbourhood suffering from multiple deprivation is one in which the population is deprived in a range of different ways.
Multiple Deprivation Index (MDI): This is a composite score using several indicators across employment, income, health, education, housing, access and child poverty categories. The higher the score, the worse the multiple deprivation. In the 2000 survey, the worst area in the UK was Benchill in Manchester with a score of 83.77 (see Figure 4); the best area was Aldenham East in Hertsmere with a score of 1.16.

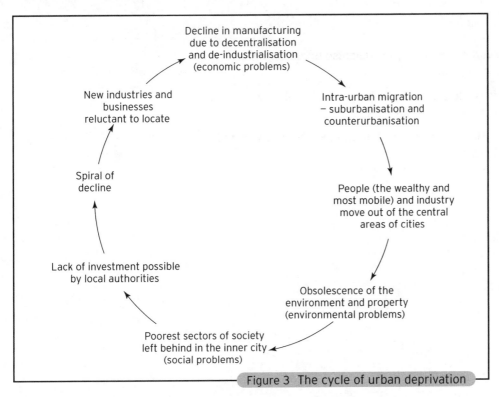

Figure 3 The cycle of urban deprivation

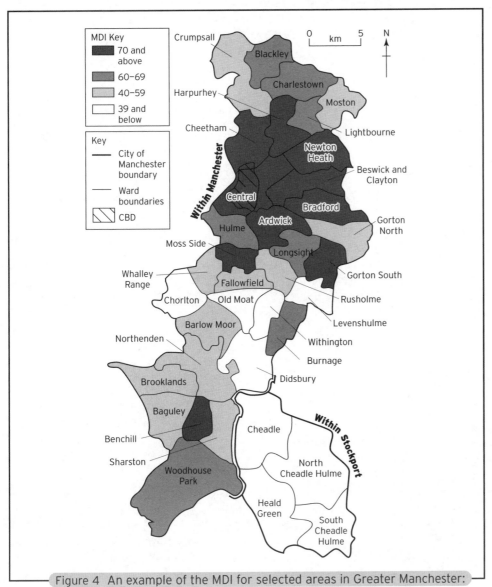

Figure 4 An example of the MDI for selected areas in Greater Manchester:

Quick check questions

1 Suggest what fieldwork techniques you could use to measure the quality of life in your local area.

2 Compare the quality of life profiles for a typical MEDC city and a LEDC city. In what ways are they similar and different?

3 Explain the trend in MDI with distance from the CBD, for the selected wards in Greater Manchester.

The Brown Agenda and sustainability

In this section, you will be revising:

- **definitions of key concepts, such as Brown Agenda and sustainability**
- **an awareness of the issues and types of sustainability of rapidly growing cities**

- **examples of issues in unsustainable LEDC and MEDC cities and ways that cities have addressed sustainability issues.**

The Brown Agenda consists of two distinct components that affect LEDC cities.

- Traditional environmental issues caused by the limited availability of good quality land, shelter and services such as clean water.
- Problems which have arisen as a result of rapid urbanisation/industrialisation such as toxic/hazardous waste, air and noise pollution, and industrial accidents from poor health and safety standards.

It is often the low-income groups that are affected most by these issues. Sustainability is

'meeting the needs of the present without compromising the ability of future generations to meet their own needs'

(Bruntland Commission, 1987).

> **Reminder**
>
> Look at section 2.8 on Managing environmental problems (pages 93–94) for details on how Los Angeles is tackling some such issues.

The sustainability of rapidly growing cities

A city can be viewed as a system with inputs and outputs. Figure 1 below contrasts an unsustainable city with a sustainable one.

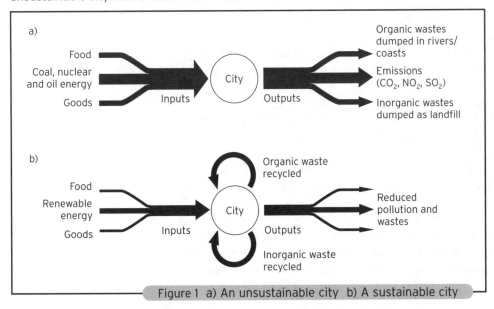

Figure 1 a) An unsustainable city b) A sustainable city

Sustainability city management can be considered under three QOL aspects:

- minimising damage to the environment and the use of resources
- providing employments and livelihoods
- providing reasonable QoL, including access to education and medical services and political freedom.

A city's 'ecological footprint' is related to the amount of productive land required to provide it with wood, water and food, as well as the disposal of its waste. This idea

> **Key concept**
>
> **Over-urbanisation** occurs when the rate of population growth, boosted by in-migration from surrounding rural areas, is more rapid than growth of the city's economy. The result is that the city is unable to provide sufficient jobs and housing. It is found in some cities in LEDCs.

was developed by William Rees in 1992. London, for example, requires an area 125 times as large as the city itself to support it. In addition, waste from the city is sent more than 120km away for disposal in landfill sites.

The ecological footprint of a city can be minimised by:

- increasing food production in the city through city farming. In New York, for example, over 1000 vacant pieces of land have been reclaimed as city gardens
- reducing or recycling waste through composting, re-use of water and the recycling of materials, including building materials, through recycling centres or separate collections for bottles, cans, newspapers, and so on
- campaigning to buy more locally-produced food, for example, at farmers' markets.

Case study of Curitiba: a model sustainable city in south-west Brazil

Although Curitiba has gown from 300,000 in 1950 to over 2.2m in 2000, the city has avoided the worst of the usual problems of congestion, pollution, under-employment, unsanitary living conditions and squatter settlements. Curitiba's urban master plan promoted sustainability. The key points are as follows.

- Extensive urban green space has been developed with seventeen new parks in recent years; one and a half million trees have been planted.
- Areas prone to flooding have been turned into wetland habitats rather than being developed.
- Bus routes and cycle paths have been integrated into the city and park areas. The road network and public transport routes have been kept to five prescribed axes. Each axis has a central road containing two express bus lanes and is flanked by local roads. One block away to either side run high-capacity one-way streets running into and out of the central city.
- These axes have become the centres for offices and commerce.
- Public transport is high quality and cheap to use. A single fare allows transfer from express routes to local buses. Extra wide doors and double/triple length buses allow for rush-hour crowds.
- The bus companies are paid by the distance of road they serve not the number of passengers. This ensures that all areas of the city are served including the slum areas.
- The city centre is pedestrianised.
- Recycling of all forms of waste products is given high priority. The urban poor can exchange their waste for free bus tickets or additional food. The city currently recycles two-thirds of its waste.
- There is a commitment to involve all citizens in decision-making at all levels, but with a particular emphasis on local neighbourhood groups. This is coupled with environmental education programmes.
- The urban poor are involved in development projects. For example, street children are paid to maintain parks and clean streets and recent migrants sort rubbish. Shops and industries are encouraged to adopt orphaned children and to provide a small wage, food and education in exchange for light maintenance and gardening chores.

> **Reminder**
>
> Think about your home area. What initiatives have been started to address sustainability? In the UK, many of these are promoted in Agenda 21 literature, which is written by local authorities and is available from many public libraries.

Quick check questions

1 What are the differences between the two systems in Figure 1?

2 Explain why Curitiba is seen as sustainable.

2.8   Managing environmental problems

In this section, you will be revising:

- awareness of the challenges of managing environmental problems in LEDC and MEDC cities
- examples of attempts to resolve or manage such challenges

- the unsustainability of current trends in car ownership, congestion, pollution and waste management.

Managing environmental issues in cities

Most large cities face the challenge of environmental issues such as:

- waste products and waste disposal, for example, Fresh Kills landfill, New York City
- air pollution from factories and exhaust fumes, for example, Los Angeles and Mexico City
- water pollution from leaking industrial waste, sewers and household waste from slum areas
- water supply: over-abstraction of water can lead to subsidence and flooding, for example, Bangkok
- transport issues such as growing car ownership and congestion, for example, Bangkok.

Such environmental problems change depending on the stage of economic development that a country or region fits into. For example, a lack of basic services and uncontrolled housing development are a feature of LEDCs, whereas MEDCs are more focused on waste disposal and growing car ownership.

Case study of Los Angeles

Temperature inversion layer frequently develops due to cooler onshore breezes and emissions of pollutants:
- traps pollution under this 'lid' effect
Higher levels of sunshine:
- photochemical smog mixed with coastal fog
- On twelve days per year, carbon monoxide levels exceed national standard (1989: 60 days)
- Health problems: in 1996 approximately 6000 deaths due to respiratory diseases related to air pollution (cost the region $10bn per year)
- On more than 100 days per year, ozone levels exceed national standard (reduced to 30 days by 1997)

High land values:
- competition for land and prime sites (CBD and suburbs) has made property expensive to buy or rent

Traffic congestion:
- travel rate index = 1.55
- annual delay per driver of 56 hours
- annual congestion costs $12570 million ($1000 per driver)
- only 4 per cent of work trips are made by public transport
- 58,000 megajoules of 'gasoline' used per person per year

Landslides and mudflows have increased in number and frequency due to urbanisation and the removal of vegetation, cutting of roads through steep hillsides, channelling rivers. This is especially a problem in the surrounding hills.

Rapid population growth:
- metropolitan area = 15.7 million; LA County = 9 million (2 million of which are Hispanics). (100,000 in 1900)
- Growing immigrant population, many are men of working age, some of whom arrive as illegal immigrants from Mexico and Central America
- Immigrants have little money and few qualifications so can only obtain low paid/informal jobs
- Lack of affordable housing (immigrants pay up to 34 per cent of their income for housing)
- Overcrowded living conditions, for example, Watt has 55 per cent of Hispanics living in congested conditions
- There is some racial tension

LOS ANGELES

Most buildings have and use air conditioning.
Many houses in the suburbs have swimming pools: 1287 litres of water is used per person per day.

There is a physical shortage of space as the LA basin is surrounded by mountains and the sea, therefore new houses have to be built on unsuitable land

Water supply:
- the city is built on the edge of a desert, so water has to be transferred long distances (via aqueducts) from north California and the Colorado River

Urban sprawl: built up area extends over 86,000km2 (115km east to west); urban density is 25 people per hectare
Development of edge cities/exurbs, such as Mission Viejo, Orange County:
- population 80,740 (1998)
- increase of 10.4 per cent since 1990
- problems of commuting (82 per cent of residents travel alone in cars to work)
- insufficient community recreation
- social problems of youth gangs and 'latch-key' kids of working parents

Earthquake zone: LA lies on San Fernando and Santa Monica Faults, and adjacent to the San Andreas Fault. In 1994, an earthquake measuring 6.7 on the Richter scale killed 60 people, injured thousands and damaged buildings. The 'big one' is expected at any time.

Figure 1 Los Angeles: an unsustainable MEDC city

Initiatives towards making Los Angeles more sustainable

Recently, a neighbourhood group took legal action against LANCER (Los Angeles City Energy Recovery Project) for siting an incinerator in their African-American neighbourhood of LA

The water authorities paid for the All American Canal to be lined to stop seepage and therefore gained the water saved for the city water supply

Improvements in engine performance to ensure a more efficient use of fuel:
• introduction of catalytic converters (since 1977)
• annual inspections of engine performance
• introduction of low-VOC reformulated petrol under the 1990 South California Clean Air Act

Pollution and resource use

Improvements in public transport:
• In 1994, a Bus Riders' Union was formed to campaign for better bus services to give access by poor families to employment and leisure opportunities
• Plans to extend the subway and development of a city light rail system

High occupancy lanes (HOVs), restricting use to vehicles with two or more occupants. LA has 480km of HOV lanes.

Development of alternative fuels (ZEVs or LPG):
• In 1995, South California set standards requiring 2 per cent of vehicles on the region's road to be ZEVs (zero emission vehicles – using fuel cells: $H + O_2$)
• This figure is set to rise to 10 per cent in later years
• Various fuel initiatives between 1990 and 1997 have produced a decrease in the number of days above national level from 165 to 27 for ozone and from 55 to 10 for carbon monoxide

Figure 2 Pollution and resource use in Los Angeles

Redevelopment of the downtown area of Los Angeles

The following steps were taken to work towards a more compact city, that is, to encourage **re-urbanisation** and reduce sprawl.

- First downtown movie studio opened at the old Unocal headquarters.
- Standard hotel (twelve storeys, built in 1956) has been converted into apartments with a bar and pool on the roof space.
- Caltrans, the award winning transportation agency building, also includes a large landscaped plaza and green space.
- Gehry's Walt Disney Concert Hall, a stainless steel sail-like structure, opened in 2003. Condos nearby doubled in value between 1998 and 2000.
- 'Our Lady of the Angels' is a new cathedral designed by an eminent Spanish architect, Rafael Moneo. Costing $189m, it is part of a newly-pedestrianised cultural corridor which also attracts crowds at lunchtime.
- St Vibiana's Cathedral has been converted into an arts centre and high-density apartments. Tax incentives are given to developers for this type of work.
- SCI-Arc, the design school, has recently moved into a renovated rail freight terminal building in the Little Tokyo downtown area.

'Young pioneers' are moving back into the city centre, attracted by the affordable rents and a change in attitudes that urban living is 'cool'. There is also the emergence of a 24-hour community based on the art scene: artist studios, galleries, museums, and so on.

Quick check questions

1. Outline how the type of environmental problems change with economic development.

2. What other initiatives could Los Angeles put in place to improve the city's sustainability?

Reminder

For a contrasting case study, look at Bangkok in *Changing Environments*, Heinemann 2000.

Key concept

Re-urbanisation: the process whereby towns and cities which have been experiencing a loss of population are able to reverse the decline and begin to grow again. Some form of city centre redevelopment is often the catalyst that starts re-urbanisation.

Reminder

Try to learn some examples of schemes to address the unsustainable environmental problems of a particular city.

Managing housing stock

In this section, you will be revising:

- **an awareness of the challenges of housing provision in LEDC and MEDC cities**
- **brownfield versus greenfield issues**

- **examples of attempts to resolve or manage such challenges.**

There are several challenges to managing housing problems in both MEDCs and LEDCs. Key ones are shown in Figure 1.

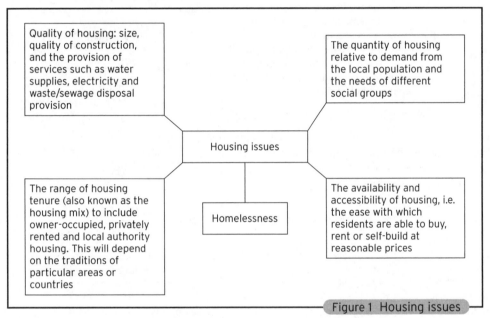

Quality of housing: size, quality of construction, and the provision of services such as water supplies, electricity and waste/sewage disposal provision

The quantity of housing relative to demand from the local population and the needs of different social groups

Housing issues

The range of housing tenure (also known as the housing mix) to include owner-occupied, privately rented and local authority housing. This will depend on the traditions of particular areas or countries

Homelessness

The availability and accessibility of housing, i.e. the ease with which residents are able to buy, rent or self-build at reasonable prices

Figure 1 Housing issues

> **Reminder**
>
> For the consideration of developments on greenfield or brownfield sites, see section 2.5, Competition and conflicts in the rural-urban fringe, pages 84–86.

The situation in MEDCs

Housing issues	Possible solutions
Inner city housing has become multi-lets, rundown and has a mixture of land use	Inner city regeneration: ○ slum clearance ○ housing action areas ○ **gentrification** (might improve the local environment) ○ re-urbanisation of derelict areas
Outer city local authority estates which have become deprived	Government initiatives such as City Challenge or SRB schemes can include outer estate areas
Housing costs have become too high for essential workers in some areas, (e.g. South East England)	○ Rental sector encouraged ○ Increase in housing association developments ○ More flexible and longer mortgage schemes

Table 1 Housing provision in MEDCs

> **Key concept**
>
> **Gentrification:** the process by which relatively affluent households move into run-down inner city neighbourhoods, thereby improving living conditions. Original housing features are often restored as part of this development. This process usually involves individuals, but large-scale restoration projects to provide housing for well-off residents may also be a type of gentrification, such as London Docklands, which was renovated by an Urban Development Corporation.

The situation in LEDCs

Housing issues	Possible solutions
Inner slum areas	▢ Construction of new public housing near areas of employment ▢ Relocation of some groups to new towns outside the city ▢ Encourage slum upgrading through the subsidised cost of building materials
Squatter settlements, especially new shanty areas on the fringe of the city or in 'problem' areas such as along river sides, on steep hill sides or adjacent to main roads	▢ Self-help schemes ▢ Encouraging extension of house finance schemes to include self-build arrangements ▢ Site-and-services programmes ▢ Community schemes to improve the environment, housing quality and community facilities ▢ Encourage the development of facilities in shanty areas such as schools and small businesses to support the informal employment sector

Table 2 Housing provision in LEDCs

In the UK there have been several phases of initiatives since the reconstruction phase after the Second World War in 1945 to address the housing quality in run-down areas of large cities. These schemes often look at general living conditions and environmental quality. The latest is a regeneration scheme (Table 3).

Reminder

New towns are another means that has been used to address poor housing. See section 2.5, Competition and conflicts in the rural-urban fringe, pages 84–86, for more details.

Period and approach	Features	Programmes and policies	Brief evaluation
1991–2001 Regeneration	Greater involvement of community and local authorities; more co-ordination of programmes and policies; focus on sustainable development and heritage conservation; combined programmes on health, education, training, crime and housing; more use of brownfield sites; access to National Lottery and EU funding	1991 City Challenge; 1993 Single Regeneration Budget; 1994 English Partnerships; 1998 Urban Task Force; 1998 New Deal for Communities; 1998 Neighbourhood Renewal Fund; 2001 Urban Regeneration Companies	Successes: ▢ Regeneration programmes are likely to be more successful because bids have to be well thought out if they are to succeed against the competition ▢ These policies have probably been more successful in developing partnerships between the different agencies operating in the inner city Failures: ▢ Local councils have to put much effort into preparing bids for government money. This effort is wasted if the bid is not successful ▢ Some areas which used to receive funding on the basis of need no longer receive funding because their bid was unsuccessful ▢ Resources are thinly spread over large areas

Table 3 Summary of the regeneration phase in the UK

Case studies of housing projects from selected LEDCs

Self-help scheme, Lusaka, Zambia

- Encouraged approximately 25 people to group together.
- They were given a standpipe and 8ha of land. The group dug the ditches and foundations, then, with the money saved, the authorities laid water and drainage pipes.
- Local craftsmen built the shells of the housing, the group were supplied with low-priced building materials and the council added electricity, tarmac roads and a school with the money saved.
- This type of scheme can also strengthen community links.

Slum clearance scheme, the Cingupura Project, Sâo Paulo

- Began in 1991.
- Replacement of hundreds of Sao Paulo's favelas with low-rise blocks of flats.
- Residents were housed temporarily in barracks during construction.
- Once moved back, they were given a low-interest 20-year mortgage with which to buy their flat.
- The scheme aims to re-house 92,000 families (half a million people) from 243 favelas.
- There may be an issue of keeping up with mortgage repayments.

Local authority favela (shanty) improvement scheme, Bairro Project, Rio de Janeiro

- 120 favelas affected.
- Began in 1994.
- £200m was spent to improve living conditions.
- Early wooden buildings replaced with larger brick-built housing.
- Widening of selected streets to allow access for emergency and waste collection vehicles.
- Laying of street pavements, concrete paths, water pipes and electricity cables.
- Used labour from within the favelas to develop resident's skills.

New town development, Barra de Tijuca or the 'new' Rio

- A self-contained city built along the coastal road from Rio de Janeiro.
- Wealthy residents have moved out to this new town to live in spacious apartments protected by security guards.
- There are also some one- to two-storey detached dwellings in the development.
- It contains a large shopping complex, schools, hospitals, offices and leisure amenities, and an efficient local bus service.
- However, this area has started to develop its own favelas as people seek work as cleaners and gardeners from people who live in these houses.

> **Key concept**
>
> **Self-help scheme:** the government begins the process of improvement in informal settlement areas by installing basic services such as electricity, a clean water supply and sewage disposal facilities. This encourages residents to improve their homes by their own efforts by, for example, replacing temporary constructions with brick-built houses.

QUICK CHECK — Quick check questions

1 What are the advantages and the disadvantages of gentrification for inner city areas?

2 Summarise the schemes used to tackle housing in a named LEDC city you have studied.

3 Outline possible strategies to address the problem of homelessness in MEDCs and LEDCs.

1. The graph below shows population change in London between 1801 and 2001.

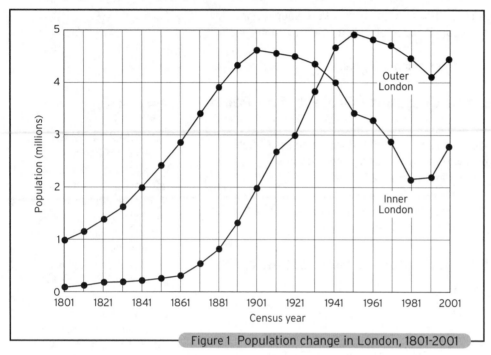

Figure 1 Population change in London, 1801-2001

   i)   Describe the changes that took place in London's population between 1801 and 2001. (4)

   ii) Name, and give reasons for, the main urban process occurring in each of the following periods.
       ● 1801 to 1901
       ● 1901 to 1981 (6)

2. Study the map below, which shows the growth of megacities.

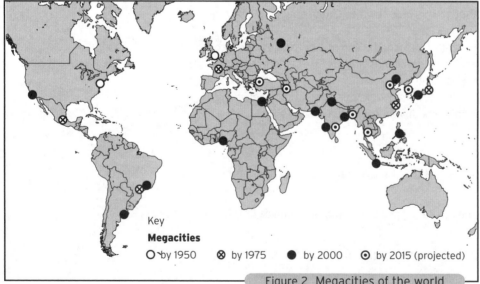

Key
Megacities
○ by 1950   ⊗ by 1975   ● by 2000   ⊙ by 2015 (projected)

Figure 2 Megacities of the world

2. *Continued*
   i) Describe the changing pattern of megacities in terms of their
      number and their geographical distribution. (4)
   ii) Suggest reasons for this changing pattern. (5)

3. Study the graph below, which shows changes in land use along a 2000m
   transect outwards from the town centre.

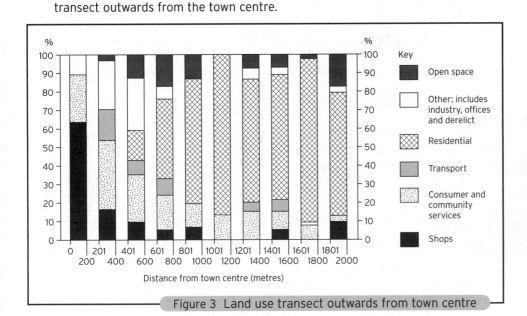

Figure 3 Land use transect outwards from town centre

   i) At what distance from the town centre do you think the limit of the
      CBD occurs? Justify your answer. (3)
   ii) Explain why land use changes along a transect from the CBD to the
       edge of the town. (4)

4. State three characteristics of a typical CBD in a MEDC. (3)

5. Examine the factors that have encouraged out-of-town shopping
   developments. (5)

6. Outline the advantages and disadvantages of building new towns. (6)

7. Study the diagram below, which show some recent developments in the centre of a British town. Suggest how these developments might help to regenerate the CBD. (6)

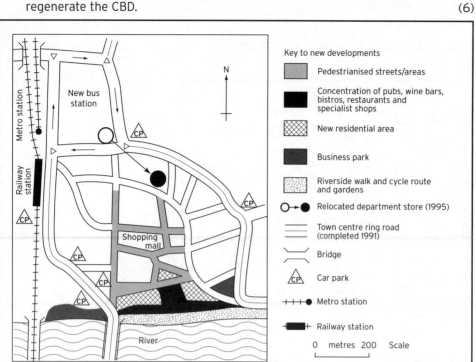

Figure 4

8. Compare the characteristics of the rural-urban fringe in LEDCs with those of MEDCs. (6)

9. With reference to named urban areas in LEDCs, examine how decision makers and planners have attempted to improve the quality of life for residents. (10)

10. With reference to specific examples, examine how urban areas may be made more sustainable. (10)

2.11 Rurality and the rural-urban continuum

In this section, you will be revising:

- rurality and what can be used to define a rural area
- changing rurality with development, with examples
- the rural-urban continuum
- the perceived advantages and disadvantages of rural living.

Rurality

The definitions of 'rural areas' vary. Some examples of ways to measure rurality are shown below.

- Settlement size: many countries set a threshold population for a settlement to be classed as urban. Below this level, areas are described as rural. Unfortunately, different countries set different levels for this threshold. In the UK, the Countryside Commission has suggested that the threshold is 10,000.
- Regional context: this is difficult to quantify. It is what the settlement is 'known' as.
- Land use: in simple terms this reflects how 'built-up' an area is. Housing development tends to be classified as 'urban', while agriculture and forests then to be classed as 'rural'.
- Population densities: rural areas are usually sparsely populated.
- Employment: often urban areas are dominated by employment in secondary or tertiary sectors, while there is often more primary work in rural areas.
- Level of services provided: urban areas are central places that contain a wide range of services. Many of these services are classed as high order, for example, department stores, jewellers. A village in a rural area is likely to contain low-order services such as a general shop or mini supermarket, a newsagent and a pub.
- Administration: councils are often identified as rural district or parish councils.
- Character: urban areas display an urban lifestyle or 'urbanism' that reflects a pace of life, anonymity, and upwardly mobile attitude.
- An index or rurality.

An index of rurality uses various indicators to create an overall index or value for how 'rural' the area is. In 1977, Cloke devised a scale known as the Cloke Index which produced five graduations of rural through to urban. He took a number of characteristics of rural areas and used census data of rural indicators (Table 1).

> **Reminder**
>
> For more detail on using settlement size to define a 'rural' area see section 2.1, The urbanisation cycle (page 73).

> **Key concept**
>
> **Ruralisation**: an increase in the proportion of people classified as living in rural areas.

Indicators used by Cloke to calculate the index:
Female population aged 15–45
Occupational structure
Population change, 1961–71
Commuting pattern, i.e. the number of people working outside the settlement
Distance from an urban centre of 50,000 people or more
Population over 65
Household amenities
Population density
Inward-migration over the previous five years

Table 1 The Cloke Index of rurality

It may be considered that the indicators used by Cloke are not appropriate today or for LEDCs. Alternative indicators for LEDCs may include:

- percentage employed in agriculture
- proximity to a school or health centre/clinic
- access to the mains electricity
- literacy levels
- percentage with access to the telephone or Internet access.

The advantages and disadvantages of rural living

Advantages of living in rural areas and villages	Disadvantages of living in rural areas and villages
<ul><li>Good sense of community</li><li>Greater availability of land and space</li><li>Less congestion and pollution</li><li>Better quality of life</li><li>Perceived to be safer</li><li>Good range of community activities, e.g. recreational groups and clubs, village hall, village newsletter, public notice board.</li></ul>	<ul><li>Remote from urban services such as hospitals, secondary schools, cinemas, restaurants</li><li>Public transport services may be infrequent or unavailable</li><li>Shop prices may be higher with a lower range of products</li><li>Few activities for teenagers</li><li>Village life may be perceived as insular and nosy.</li></ul>

Table 2 Advantages and disadvantages of rural living

The rural-urban continuum

Even with such indices, it is difficult to distinguish between rural and urban areas. It is perhaps more helpful to see rural and urban as different ends of a continuum. The rural-urban continuum (Figure 1) is the gradual change from predominantly urban characteristics to predominantly rural characteristics at the edge of an urban settlement, rather than a distinct line where urban settlement ends and rural settlement begins.

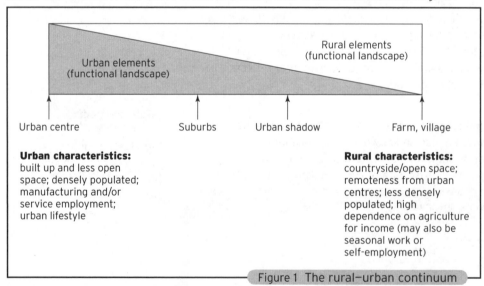

Figure 1 The rural–urban continuum

Changes in the rural–urban continuum occur over time and spatially.

Quick check questions

1 Think about what indicators might be more appropriate for a rurality index in the UK today.

2 Identify the advantages and disadvantages of living in a rural area of a region of a LEDC.

3 Think about the advantages and disadvantages of living in a rural area a) in a MEDC, b) in a LEDC.

In this section, you will be revising:

- **factors that influence the 'look' of different rural landscapes**
- **Global patterns of rurality.**

Factors that influence rural landscapes (Figure 1) are shown below.

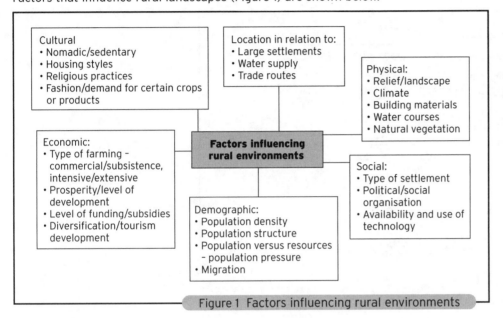

Figure 1 Factors influencing rural environments

The patterns of rurality generally reflect levels of economic development:

- spatially
- over time.

Spatial patterns

Some examples of the spatial patterns of rurality (percentage rural) compared with HDI (Human Development Index) of various countries are given below (Table 1).

Country	Percentage rural	HDI	Country	Percentage rural	HDI
Australia	15.3	0.93	Nigeria	60.7	0.44
Germany	13.5	0.91	Tanzania	75.6	0.41
UK	10.5	0.92	Malaysia	46.3	0.77
Japan	22.4	0.92	Somalia	74.3	0.43
USA	23.8	0.93	Egypt	55.2	0.62
Italy	33.4	0.90	Burkino Faso	72.8	0.30

Table 1 Rurality compared with HDI for selected countries

The change in the number and proportion of people living in rural areas varies over time too. In many MEDCs, urbanisation occurred throughout the nineteenth century associated with the industrialisation process. In LEDCs, this has happened late in the twentieth century, again linked to economic development but over a much shorter time span than for MEDCs.

A picture of the changing trends for particular countries can be obtained from graphs of the changing percentages of rural and urban population over a period of time (Figure 2).

Reminder

For more details on the urbanisation cycle see section 2.1 The urbanisation cycle, pages 73–4.

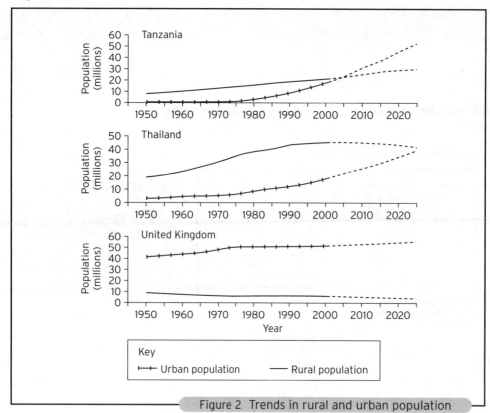

Figure 2 Trends in rural and urban population

 Quick check questions

1 Look at Figure 5.2 on page 59 in *Changing Environments*, Heinemann 2000. What factors appear to have produced the rural area in the middle ground of the photograph?

2 Compare the trends in rural and urban population shown in each of the examples in Figure 2.

3 Suggest reasons for the difference in the graphs.

In this section, you will be revising:

- **the processes of change in MEDC rural areas that can lead to growth**
- **the impacts of these changes.**

In both MEDCs and LEDCs rural areas are undergoing change (Figure 1).

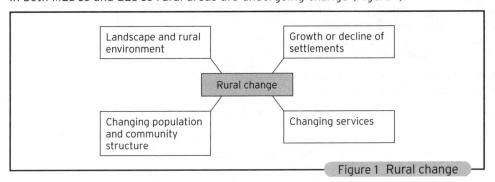

Landscape and rural environment

Growth or decline of settlements

Rural change

Changing population and community structure

Changing services

Figure 1 Rural change

Reminder

Consider a rural area that you have studied. How has it changed and what are the key reasons for this change?

Key factors that affect rural change include the following:

- proximity to large urban area(s)
- accessibility
- natural beauty
- planning decisions
- land reform
- agricultural changes or innovations
- diversification and tourism development.

The processes of change produce either growth or decline, creating a cycle (see Figure 2)

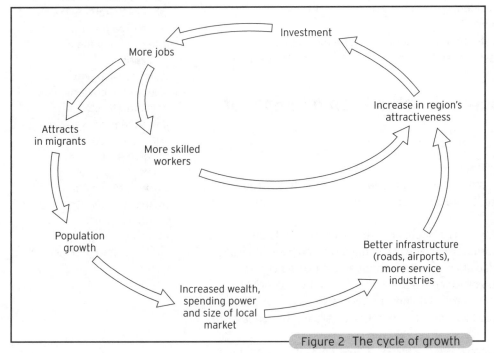

Investment

More jobs

Attracts in migrants

More skilled workers

Population growth

Increased wealth, spending power and size of local market

Better infrastructure (roads, airports), more service industries

Increase in region's attractiveness

Figure 2 The cycle of growth

Key concepts

Rural–urban fringe: the area that imprecisely marks the boundary between countryside and urban areas. This zone possess some characteristics of both a rural and an urban environment

Fragmentation occurs when agricultural land is broken up so that one farm may actually consist of numerous small fields scattered over a wide area, often the result of inheritance laws.

Some key reasons for growth in rural areas are identified in Table 1.

Reasons for change	Examples of consequences for rural areas
Changes in farming practice, such as high-yielding varieties (HYVs) of crops, use of fertilisers and pesticides, improvements in technology or a move to agri-business	Removal of hedgerows and increasing size of fields to enable mechanisation Wetland areas may be drained to increase crop production area Pesticides may reduce biodiversity Increased arable farming, unless carefully managed, increases soil erosion Increased use of fertilisers may increase pollution in nearby rivers and eutrophication in ponds Factory-style farming is often accompanied by large, characterless buildings and farms may merge to become larger units Subsidies may encourage particular crops or livestock which directly affects the look of the landscape High Yielding Varieties (HYVs) may result in other issues such as the need for irrigation in dry periods
Diversification of farming activity	Change in the landscape away from traditional agriculture towards recreation and leisure activities
Counterurbanisation and the growth of villages in rural areas	Suburbanisation and expansion of the village around the original core Change in village character to a commuter village More executive housing and pressure on health and education services A decline in the traditional services such as the village shop Tourist villages may experience an increase in second home ownership, boosting house prices Farms or barns may be converted and sold as housing **Teleworking** has meant the expansion of high speed telecommunication links such as broadband Internet access

Table 1 Key changes in rural areas of growth

Conflicts can result from these changes between competing land uses and between competing groups of people.

Examples of possible conflicts are between:

- newcomers and established residents in a suburbanised rural village
- recreational walkers and farmers
- mineral extraction and the protection of ecologically valuable sites
- water skiing and the use of faster speed boats on lakes that are also used by sailing clubs.

A case study of Ploeren, Brittany: an example of an expanded village

- Ploeren is located in South Brittany, 5km from the coast.
- It has experienced rapid population growth in the last 20 years (from around 900 in 1962 to 4000 today), due to its proximity to the growing city of Vannes and the Nantes–Brest Expressway.
- The original settlement developed as a nodal point of two main roads but in recent years it has developed as a dormitory village for Vannes with an widening range of services such as new leisure facilities, primary school and shopping centre.
- Most new houses are detached or executive style and are located on private estates; 2 per cent of houses are second homes; there is also some social housing.
- The area covered by the village has also expanded northwards to the edge of the expressway and to the east.
- The population now includes more young families. 32 per cent of the population are <20 years old; only 3 per cent are >75 years old. 93 per cent of the population own at least one car, which is a comparatively high figure. All of these statistics are significantly higher than the region as a whole.

Key concepts

Rural diversification: a diversion of resources (land, labour, capital) previously committed to rural activities into non-traditional enterprises.
Rural growth pole: a rural area where governments deliberately encourage investment and resources to stimulate economic development.
Teleworking: people working from home linked by telecommunications (phone, fax, Internet, modems, video-conferencing) to their office.

A case study of Ashwell, Hertfordshire: an example of village suburbanisation

- Ashwell has grown by 25 per cent since 1971, due to the influx of new residents who have moved from London. The current population is approximately 1650.
- The variety of buildings in the village contribute to Ashwell's character. Recent expansion has been provided for by:
  - a 1980s new housing development
  - barn conversions
  - new houses on the edge of the village
  - 'in-fill' whereby gaps between older, lower density housing are used for building; this increases the density of the village core
  - retention of most of the village services but a change in emphasis to include a take away, bank, estate agent, craft businesses, health services, kennels, child minders and five pubs, as well as low-order shops. This compares with mainly agricultural and brewery employment in 1924.
- The village population is ageing in line with trends in the rest of the UK. One fifth of residents are retired, but many also commute the 40-minute rail journey into London.
- There is an increasing gap in the village between higher-income earners who can afford the rising costs of housing and commuting, and those on lower salaries such as trainees, farm workers and first-time buyers who are looking for smaller and cheaper properties.
- The area is earmarked for further expansion as part of the government's commitment to increase the supply and density of housing in the South East, with 4400 new houses to be developed in North Hertfordshire by 2010.

In considering changes in rural areas it must also remembered that there are many links between urban and rural areas (Figure 4). Counterurbanisation, therefore, has an impact on both rural and urban areas.

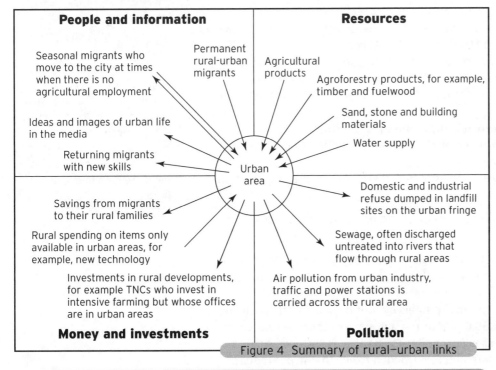

People and information

Seasonal migrants who move to the city at times when there is no agricultural employment

Permanent rural–urban migrants

Ideas and images of urban life in the media

Returning migrants with new skills

Urban area

Resources

Agricultural products

Agroforestry products, for example, timber and fuelwood

Sand, stone and building materials

Water supply

Savings from migrants to their rural families

Rural spending on items only available in urban areas, for example, new technology

Investments in rural developments, for example TNCs who invest in intensive farming but whose offices are in urban areas

Domestic and industrial refuse dumped in landfill sites on the urban fringe

Sewage, often discharged untreated into rivers that flow through rural areas

Air pollution from urban industry, traffic and power stations is carried across the rural area

Money and investments

Pollution

Figure 4 Summary of rural–urban links

Quick check questions

1 Try to think of an example you have studied of agricultural change. How has this change affected the rural landscape?

2 Identify two examples of conflicts in a rural area that you have studied. Describe how these have been resolved.

Change and conflict in MEDC rural areas: decline areas

In this section, you will be revising:

- **the processes of change in MEDC rural areas that can lead to decline**

- **the impacts of these changes.**

Changes in rural areas leads to a cycle of decline (Figure 1). For an example, use the case study of Cornwall below.

Case study: Cornwall

- On average wages are £88 lower than the national average; two of the districts in the county are amongst England's most deprived areas.
- It is in a peripheral location in the UK compared with the core region of the South East. Its remoteness from major cities and urban markets makes it less desirable for companies to locate there.
- Rail links are slow and often expensive at peak times.
- Nationally, agricultural employment declined by 14 per cent between 1987 and 1997 which continued an earlier trend due to the mechanisation of farming.
- The collapse in beef and dairy prices in the 1990s resulted in a shift to arable farming (which requires fewer employees), and/or diversification which has resulted in the sale of farm buildings and land.
- Other traditional industries such as fishing (at St Ives and Padstow) and china clay extraction (mainly at St Austell Moor), have also declined.
- Many families and first time buyers cannot afford to purchase homes but the 'right-to-buy' scheme of the late 1980s reduced the amount of social/local authority housing in rural areas. The last 20 years has also seen an increase in homelessness in rural areas.
- Cornwall's population is older than in most other parts of the UK (20 per cent >64yrs compared with a UK average of 15.8 per cent) resulting from a trend for people to retire to the county.
- This has implications, since the incomes of the elderly are lower and they often need more health resources.

Attempts to change the fortunes of Cornwall focused on diversification into recreation and tourism.

- Population has grown by 27 per cent and its working population by 24 per cent since 1983, which is at a higher rate than the UK average but this growth varies across the county.
- Every year the population of the county swells by four million visitors spending £930m. Tourism accounts for 30,000 jobs too but many of these are seasonal. Many jobs are in small businesses (vulnerable to changes in fortunes such as during the recent foot and mouth outbreak), and in towns that might require a long journey to work for people living in more remote locations.
- Working hours are often long and more than 25 per cent of the population works more than 40 hours per week, which may be even longer during the tourist season.

Attracting development into Cornwall has focused on its formal designation as a Rural Development Area (RDA), which made it eligible for Leader programme and Objective funding. This funding is directed at small- and medium-scale businesses, tourism,

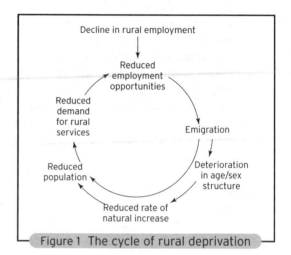

Figure 1 The cycle of rural deprivation

Key concepts

Rural depopulation: the movement of people from rural areas, usually in search of work.

Repopulation: people moving back to an area that was previously depopulated.

Rural deprivation: deprivation in a rural area, resulting from poverty, low income and a poor quality if life.

diversification of agricultural areas, training, and community regeneration. Most projects are small in scale but can be significant to village communities.

Other funding has been provided by Objective 1 and central government grants, bringing a total of £600m to the region from June 2000.

Reminder

For more details on Cornwall, see pages 220–231 in *Changing Environments*, Heinemann 2000.

Population pyramids as an indicator of rural change

Population pyramids reflect changes in village population structure (Figure 2).

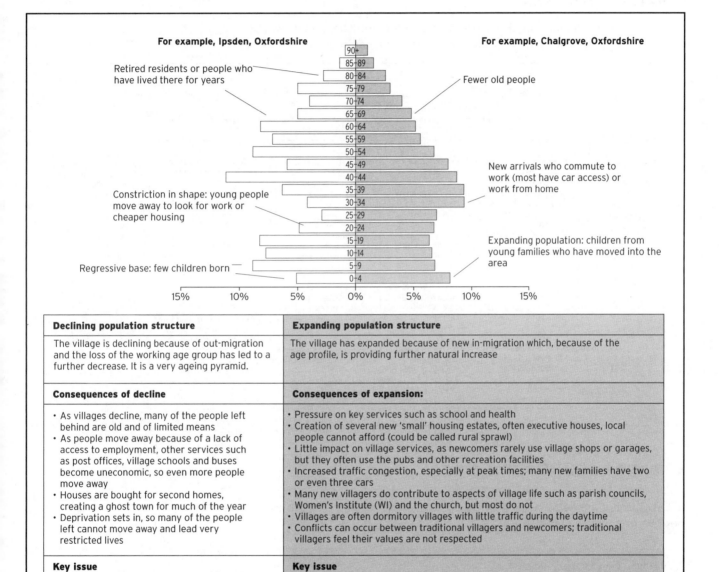

Figure 2 Expanding and declining population pyramid

 Quick check questions

1 Identify the factors that appear to have influenced Cornwall's decline.

2 Outline the benefits of the projects to rural areas in Cornwall.

3 Compare the shape of the two halves of the pyramid (Figure 2). Explain these differences.

Change and conflict in LEDC rural areas

In this section, you will be revising:

- **the processes of change in LEDC rural areas**
- **the impacts of these changes**

- **how this can lead to growth or decline.**

The rural–urban continuum in LEDCs is somewhat different from that in MEDCs (Figure 1), but accessibility to the nearby urban area still has an important influence.

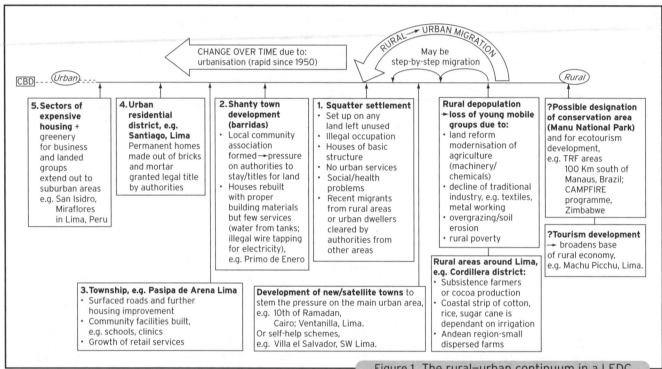

Figure 1 The rural–urban continuum in a LEDC

Change in LEDC rural areas

In LEDCs there are also a number of changes occurring in rural areas. These can be positive or negative (Table 1).

Possible changes	Impacts of changes
Out-migration	Changes in population: young, economically active sectors migrate to urban areas leaving the dependent sector in rural areas, which limits their capacity for further development.
Expansion of large urban areas	Sprawl on the periphery of urban areas into rural areas. This development is largely temporary housing for recent migrants to the city, although some housing areas may have become consolidated with the replacement of houses of more permanent materials and some services. This development will gradually encroach on farms and other rural land use close to the city.
The development of industries such as mining or tourism in particular locations	This development is likely to become a magnet for people seeking employment. There will also be a multiplier effect in that region with the knock-on development of supporting industries and services, as well as accommodation for workers, guides, and so on (i.e. secondary resources). However, there may also be negative effects with investment in this locality rather than others and the development of squatter settlements as people come to the area seeking work.

Table 1 Changes in rural areas. *(Continued on page 111.)*

Possible changes	Impacts of changes
Changes in agriculture, often towards more cash crops	This move towards cash crops for export may be at the expense of subsistence crops. This, in turn, may have an impact on the general health of rural families, an increase in the use of fertilisers and pesticides and the move towards more mechanised production methods.
Land reform	This will halt and/or remove fragmentation of pieces of land into more consolidated areas, which will mean that they are more economic to farm. However, it might also result in the migration of key workers to other rural areas or even to nearby cities for alternative work. This may give labour shortages at harvest times.
Disease outbreaks and/or the growth in the number of HIV/AIDS related problems	Direct loss of productive labour on farms or other industries due to illness itself or to look after another family member. The costs of medical care and medicines also adds an additional cost to family expenditure.

Table 1 *Continued*

Conflicts can also occur:

- between traditionalists and people who want the area to develop at a more rapid rate
- between conflicting land uses, such as between agribusiness developments and organic farming, or between the development of ecotourism projects and a large scale mining scheme
- between developers in identifying the order of priority for development projects in a particular rural area
- between residents and local government as to what form and at what pace development in the local area should take place.

Reminder

For an example of growth in a LEDC, see section 2.17 Managing recreation and tourism in the countryside, pages 108–110.

Case study: rural issues in Malawi

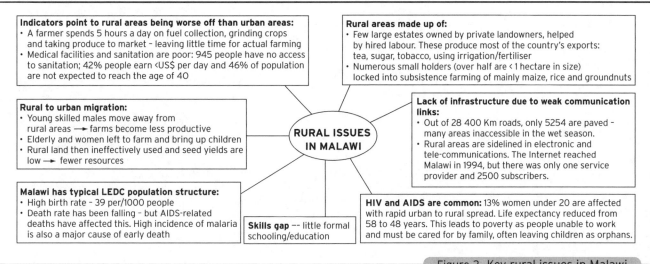

Figure 2 Key rural issues in Malawi

Examples of the ways used to resolve rural poverty in Mchinji, a province of Malawi, by the United Nations Development Program, UNDP are as follows.

- Improving maize production by promoting the use of compost from animal manure and crop residues as a fertiliser, preventing the need for expensive fertilisers.
- A move to grow crops that require little of no fertiliser such as millet, sorghum or sweet potatoes.
- Efforts by Malawi's National Agricultural Research System to develop drought-resistant maize varieties.
- Increased use of dambos (land depressions close to river banks which are naturally irrigated and fertile) for horticultural crops such as tomatoes, rice, turnips, onions and green maize. Crops are sold in local markets to generate income or to be consumed. This improves the local diet, especially during the drought season.

Reminder

For more information on the issues in Malawi, see pages 182–196 in *Changing Environments*, Heinemann 2000.

- A village health centre is being established to monitor the weight of children under five years of age.
- Adoption of contour ridging, planting of grasses along the river bank and afforestation with eucalyputus trees (with the help of the Malawian Forestry Department), to counteract the issue of soil erosion.
- A programme to provide simple water pumps to provide safe drinking water in rural villages and to establish 1000 boreholes. Villagers will also be trained how to use and maintain them, and to adopt better sanitation practices.
- Micro-credit loans and tax incentives provided by UNDP targeted towards the formation of small businesses, such as carpentry, brick-making or car/bicycle repairs. Income from these helps families to invest in education, health, clothing and to save for the future.

QUICK CHECK

Quick check questions

1 Consider a LEDC rural area that you have studied. Think of examples of changes that have occurred in the area. What impact have these changes had on the landscape and the local community?

2 What factors appear to be holding back economic development in rural areas in Malawi?

3 Think how each of these schemes will help to address poverty in Mchinji?

Key concepts

Cycle of deprivation: a sequence of events experienced by disadvantaged people in which one problem leads to another and so makes things worse.

Land reform: the re-distribution of land in an area, to increase farming output and to raise individuals' standards of living. This is likely to involve consolidation of small plots of land into large areas. This, in turn, will affect the appearance of the landscape.

In this section, you will be revising:

- **the meaning of sustainability in terms of rural development strategies**
- **examples of rural development schemes in MEDCs and LEDCs that improve the quality of the environment and the lives of the rural poor**

- **the value of integrated schemes.**

Sustainable development in terms of rural areas is development that meets the current needs of rural people but without compromising their future needs. This means that rural living standards are gradually improved but not at the expense of the rural environment. Key features of sustainable schemes in rural areas:

- small-scale and community-led schemes rather than '**top-down**' strategies
- involve people and use their skills
- low tech
- focused on the needs of local communities.

Different types of sustainability can be distinguished (Table 1).

Types of sustainability	Examples
Environmental	- Protecting more remote areas or heavily visited tourist areas via planning controls - Maintenance of greenbelt land - Regeneration of wetland and forest areas or restoring the rural landscape through set-aside schemes.
Economic	- Providing grants to local businesses in rural areas to enable them to maintain or create employment - Encouraging the development of key services in certain of the main villages where a threshold of users can be maintained
Social and political, including empowerment	- Restricting house ownership to local people or the use of housing association schemes to assist young couples to purchase a home in villages - The empowerment of village residents via consultation exercises about proposed village changes

Table 1 Types of sustainability

In addition, different strategies need to be used in different types of rural area. For example, an area on the fringe of a large urban area may have issues of conflict between developers and existing residents or conservationists. In other rural areas, the focus might be on control of second/retirement homes in villages or maintaining key services or even protection from the negative impacts of tourism development. If there is wide coverage across the different strands of sustainability then this represents an integrated approach to sustainable management.

Key concepts

Rural growth pole: a rural area where governments deliberately encourage investment and resources to stimulate economic development.

Top-down strategy: rural development projects determined and managed by people or agencies from outside the area using technology, methods and advice from MEDCs.

Bottom-up strategy: local communities have ownership and involvement in managing rural development strategies.

Case studies: rural development schemes

Case studies to develop for revision of sustainable rural development schemes are:

- Nepal, and (See websites on Nepal Annapurna Conservation area at www.Heinemann.co.uk/hotlinks, insert express code **1544S**)
- East-African projects undertaken by **NGOs** (see Figure 1).

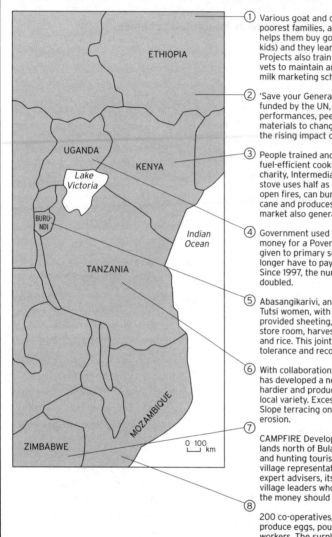

① Various goat and camel projects focused on the poorest families, and especially women. Credit helps them buy goats (repaid in kind with goat kids) and they learn to manage them effectively. Projects also train certain people as 'bare foot' vets to maintain animal health and some set up milk marketing schemes.

② 'Save your Generation Association', a local NGO funded by the UN, uses puppet drama performances, peer counsellors and education materials to change health behaviour and check the rising impact of AIDS on young Ethiopians.

③ People trained and employed to make fuel-efficient cooking stoves with help from the charity, Intermediate Technology. The improved stove uses half as much fuelwood as conventional open fires, can burn maize stalks and dry sugar cane and produces less smoke. Stoves sold at market also generate income.

④ Government used World Bank/IMF debt relief money for a Poverty Action Fund. Grants were given to primary schools so that parents no longer have to pay fees for children to attend. Since 1997, the number of pupils has more than doubled.

⑤ Abasangikarivi, an association of 500+ Hutu and Tutsi women, with the help of Oxfam which provided sheeting, seeds and tools, and rent for a store room, harvested their first crops of maize and rice. This joint association also helps tolerance and reconciliation.

⑥ With collaboration of local people FARM Africa has developed a new cross-bred bean that is hardier and produces four times the yield of the local variety. Excess stock now sold at market. Slope terracing on hillsides also helps soil erosion.

⑦ CAMPFIRE Development Projects for communal lands north of Bulawayo focused on photographic and hunting tourism. Run by a committee of village representatives, government officers and expert advisers, its profits are distributed to village leaders who discuss with local people how the money should be spent.

⑧ 200 co-operatives, with help from CAFOD, produce eggs, poultry and maize for rural workers. The surplus is sold in nearby towns. At Maputo, money has been reinvested and a new water tank has allowed expansion into pottery.

Figure 1 Selected rural community projects in East Africa

Key concepts

Non Government Organisation (NGO): a voluntary, non-political, non-commercial organisation that is neither funded nor controlled by a national government. NGOs often concern themselves with environmental issues or helping the less privileged members of society.
Intermediate technology: simple technology that is straight-forward to build, small-scale, affordable, and appropriate to local communities' needs. This type of development also promotes self-reliance and the use of local skills.

Reminder

Compare the approach in this LEDC example with an example of sustainable development in the UK in section 2.18, Managing rural deprivation and poverty, pages 120–123.

Quick check questions

1 Try to describe the details of an integrated scheme that you have studied.

2 To what extent could it be seen as sustainable?

3 Compare and contrast one of the LEDC schemes highlighted in this section with one in an MEDC that you have studied.

Managing recreation and tourism in the countryside

In this section, you will be revising:

- **the significance of tourism to the rural economy**
- **the issues associated with managing the demands of traditional and new recreation uses**
- **consequences of such management attempts**

- **evaluation and examples of appropriate strategies for rural tourism, mass tourism and ecotourism to include some MEDC examples and some LEDC examples.**

Recreation and **tourism** have developed in many rural areas, often as a result of the diversification of farming or village activities.

Recreation

Visitors to the English countryside spend around £11.5bn per year, but 75 per cent of such visitors are home-based. There are also 289,000 direct and 49,000 indirect jobs in recreation and tourism in England. In recent years recreation activities have developed beyond the traditional walking and camping to include new recreation uses for rural land and the development of **secondary resources** such as:

- accommodation: holiday cottages and bed-and-breakfast
- farm shops, tea rooms/cafés, ice cream or cheese making
- activity holidays
- craft centres
- water- and land-based sports
- war games and paint-ball activities
- game and clay pigeon shooting
- nature reserves and wildlife parks
- farm zoos
- events such as music festivals, farm open days and demonstrations
- golf courses.

Tourism

General factors that affect the growth of tourism include:

- transport links: for international tourism this includes regular charter flights with major tourist-sending countries
- historical or colonial relationships with other countries
- changing tastes and fashion
- the nature and uniqueness of natural, cultural and built attractions
- climate and **primary resources**
- government policy regarding international tourism
- the nature of the political regime in the area and its stability
- the amount of investment in secondary resources
- globalisation of the world-wide tourism industry
- influence of multi-national enterprises (MNE) and possible **leakage**.

While some of these are more applicable to international tourism, others are still relevant to the development of tourism areas within a country. Tourism is the world's fastest growing industry. Globally, there are more people employed in tourism than in any other industry. It is estimated that 10 per cent of global economic output or $400bn

Key concepts

Recreation: activities undertaken when not working, eating or sleeping.
Tourism: when people travel to areas outside their local area. This usually involves an overnight stay at the destination in order to be classed as tourism.
Primary resources: the main attractions at a destination, such as a beach or a castle. These provide the main reasons for tourists to visit the destination and can be natural or man-made.
Secondary resources: the facilities required to make the visit possible, or are needed during the visit, such as cafés, car parks, hotels, etc.
Tertiary resources: the support facilities, such as cash dispensers, toilets or signposts.

is now created by tourism. It has given many LEDCs an opportunity to improve their economies very rapidly via the **multiplier effect** (Figure 1).

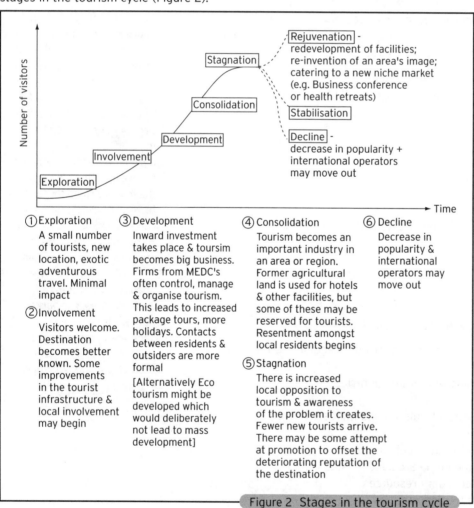

Figure 1 Tourism and the multiplier effect

Key concept

Multiplier effect: a positive multiplier effect is when the development of one activity can encourage wealth and development in other activities in the immediate area. A negative multiplier effect is associated with the decline of an area.

As an area develops as a tourist destination, it is likely to go through a series of stages in the tourism cycle (Figure 2).

Number of visitors

Rejuvenation -
redevelopment of facilities;
re-invention of an area's image;
catering to a new niche market
(e.g. Business conference
or health retreats)

Stagnation

Stabilisation

Consolidation

Development

Decline -
decrease in popularity +
international operators
may move out

Involvement

Exploration

Time

① Exploration
A small number of tourists, new location, exotic adventurous travel. Minimal impact

② Involvement
Visitors welcome. Destination becomes better known. Some improvements in the tourist infrastructure & local involvement may begin

③ Development
Inward investment takes place & tourism becomes big business. Firms from MEDC's often control, manage & organise tourism. This leads to increased package tours, more holidays. Contacts between residents & outsiders are more formal
[Alternatively Eco tourism might be developed which would deliberately not lead to mass development]

④ Consolidation
Tourism becomes an important industry in an area or region. Former agricultural land is used for hotels & other facilities, but some of these may be reserved for tourists. Resentment amongst local residents begins

⑤ Stagnation
There is increased local opposition to tourism & awareness of the problem it creates. Fewer new tourists arrive. There may be some attempt at promotion to offset the deteriorating reputation of the destination

⑥ Decline
Decrease in popularity & international operators may move out

Figure 2 Stages in the tourism cycle

Key concepts

Leakage: when the financial benefit of tourism is taken out of the host LEDC country to MEDCs via MNEs controlling much of the tourism development. Examples of leakage include:
- payment for goods imported for tourists
- payments to foreign owners of hotels and other amenities
- foreign workers sending money home
- travel costs paid to foreign airlines, cruise ships, etc.
- government repaying loans.

The impacts of the development of recreation and tourism activities can be both positive and negative (see Table 1, page 117).

To successfully develop recreation or tourism in a region, the negative impacts must be minimised and the positive ones developed further.

	Positive	Negative
Environmental	• Brightens and regenerates run-down areas • Improves and increases facilities and amenities • Pollution and heritage management • Public health benefits: water management /sewage control	• Pollution: increased visitor numbers generate more litter, waste and noise • Overcrowding and congestion • Damage to heritage resources through overuse • Land use lost to hotels, complexes, etc • Destruction of habitat • Spoiling of landscape through poorly-planned developments
Economic	• Generates wealth for all sectors • Provides employment directly and indirectly • Multiplier effect: the way money from tourism is circulated within the local economy • Provides invisible earnings for a country's balance of payments • Investment in tourism projects is a base for regeneration, e.g. the Eden Project, Cornwall	• Leakage: money lost from the local economy • Local taxes may be raised to finance facilities for tourists • House prices might rise, especially if there is an increase in second home ownership. If the cost of housing rises above what locals can afford, this may result in an out-migration, especially of local young couples • Local shops might be replaced by tourist outlets
Socio-cultural	• Increased knowledge of host culture, e.g.music and art • Improved reputation and visibility of the host area to other regions/countries • Revival of host culture for tourists • Exposure to new ideas, values and ways of life	• Loss of original identity and culture • Pressure to change values or behaviour to suit visitors • Locals have a lower status than visitors • Local art and culture is trivialised • Locals cannot afford to pay the higher prices geared for visitors' spending power • Traditional skills are lost as people turn to more profitable incomes • Tourism may introduce gambling, prostitution and drunken behaviour • Reduction in the quality of life for locals: overcrowding, noise etc.

Table 1 Impacts of tourism

Conflicts may also arise as a result of recreation and tourism development. An example of this can be seen in a National Park such as the Lake District. Look at Figure 3 below.

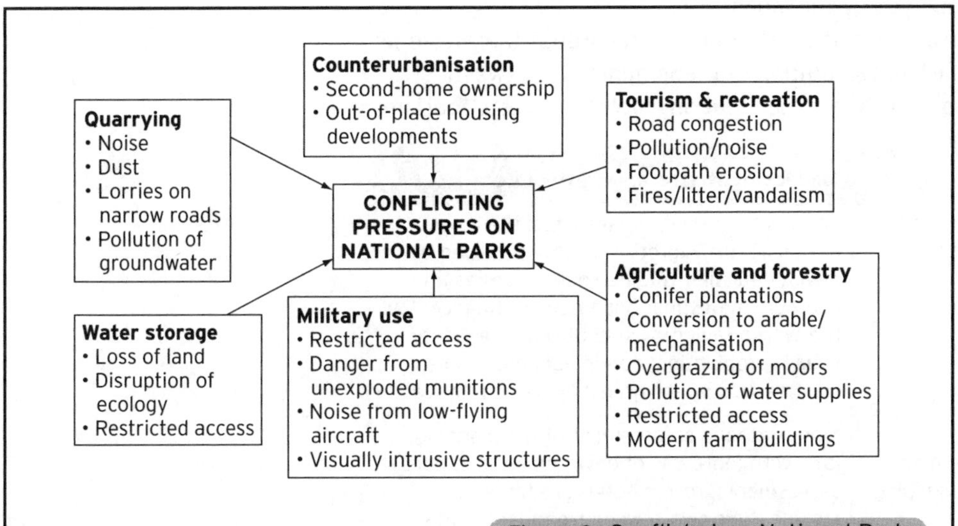

Key concepts

Mass tourism: the large-scale development of tourism attractions and facilities within an area with little regard for the impacts this will have on the local area or its people.

Ecotourism: a form of tourism which aims to conserve fragile ecosystems and market their appeal while providing income for local people.

Quarrying
• Noise
• Dust
• Lorries on narrow roads
• Pollution of groundwater

Counterurbanisation
• Second-home ownership
• Out-of-place housing developments

Tourism & recreation
• Road congestion
• Pollution/noise
• Footpath erosion
• Fires/litter/vandalism

CONFLICTING PRESSURES ON NATIONAL PARKS

Water storage
• Loss of land
• Disruption of ecology
• Restricted access

Military use
• Restricted access
• Danger from unexploded munitions
• Noise from low-flying aircraft
• Visually intrusive structures

Agriculture and forestry
• Conifer plantations
• Conversion to arable/ mechanisation
• Overgrazing of moors
• Pollution of water supplies
• Restricted access
• Modern farm buildings

Figure 3 Conflicts in a National Park

Ecotourism

Since the late 1980s, **ecotourism** has developed for a number of reasons, the main one being an increasing awareness of the environmental and social costs of traditional **mass tourism**. Many LEDCs who have viewed tourism as the key to economic development have found that many of the economic benefits are outweighed by costs. Other reasons for the growth of ecotourism include:

- the desire of affluent residents of MEDCs to visit out of the way places
- growing environmental awareness in the developed world
- growing concern about the effects of tourism
- improved access to more remote areas.

A typical ecotourist:

- is highly educated
- has a high income and social status
- is environmentally aware
- is usually resident in a developed country.

Ecotourism is also known as 'rural', 'green' or 'alternative' tourism.

Case study of issues and management of tourism

Mauritius: an example of the growth of tourism in a LEDC

Reasons for visiting:

- volcanic island in the Indian Ocean which has sandy beaches, blue-water lagoons and coral reefs; seen as a 'paradise` island
- tropical climate: 24–30°C all year and the daytime heat and humidity are offset by sea breezes
- spectacular views, for example, the Black River Gorge area
- coastal hotel resorts have developed, for example, north of Port Louis
- regular flights to key European airports and direct connections to Asia, Australia and Africa.

Tourism details:

- during the past ten years tourism numbers have doubled to around 580,000
- 20,000 people are directly employed by the industry
- there continues to be tensions between the different cultural groups that make up the resident population of the island. A rotation of prime ministers between representatives of key ethnic groups has helped, but any violence affects tourism.

Issues caused by tourism growth	Management strategies attempted
Destruction of many species of flora and fauna, with less than 2 per cent of the island containing native forest	Various conservation measures: the coral island, Ile aux Aigrettes, is now managed by MWF (Mauritian Wildlife Foundation) as an ecotourism destination; a nursery financed by the World Bank grows 45,000 native plants a year for replanting; non-indigenous plants, such as Acacia, are gradually being removed
Damage to the marine environment: disturbance from motorboats, fishermen and divers, plus rising pollution from piping untreated sewage straight into the sea	More rigorous enforcement of the planning laws with more use of environmental impact assessments; resort hotels are forced to include their own sewage treatment works into their construction plans
Sale of coral and turtle shells from the reefs to tourists	Tourists are being educated not to buy these

Table 3 Issues and strategies in Mauritius

Reminder

For a contrasting case study, look at Kinder Scout in the Peak District on pages 202–210, *Changing Environments*, Heinemann, 2000

Quick check questions

1 Why has there been growth in recreation and tourism in recent years?

2 Consider tourism areas that you have studied, or the examples given later in this section. What stage of the tourism cycle do they currently appear to be at?

3 Compare the strategies used to manage the impacts of tourism in specific areas of a MEDC and of a LEDC.

Reminder

1 For details of tourism in Vietnam, see pages 197–201 in *Changing Environments*, Heinemann 2000.
2 Look at Bloomfield lodge, Queensland, as an example of ecotourism in a MEDC and Nepal for an example of mountain tourism. Go to www.Heinemann.co.uk/hotlinks and enter express code **5144S.**

Managing rural deprivation and poverty

In this section, you will be revising:

- reasons for rural poverty
- the cycle of rural deprivation

- a range of strategies to improve levels of income and the quality of life in contrasting rural areas.

Poverty and deprivation in MEDCs

Rural areas in MEDCs are generally regarded as more affluent than many urban areas. However, some more remote rural areas have low average earnings, a low level of employment for school leavers, a lack of affordable housing for young couples and a significant number of elderly people.

Deprivation is often described as people having a standard of living that falls below what is expected in that particular society. It is usually associated with a lack of materials resources but can also include perceptions of other issues such as crime levels. It has been suggested that there are three types of rural deprivation (Table 1).

Key concepts

Rural disadvantage: the inability of individuals or households to share lifestyles open to the majority.
Rural poverty: disadvantage due to a lack of financial resources.

Types of deprivation	Focus	Reasons	Possible indicators
Household deprivation	Lack of affordable private or rental housing. Fear of crime with declining levels of local policing in rural areas.	Shortage of affordable housing because: - wealthy people retire to the area - there are strict planning restrictions in some scenic rural areas - rural gentrification is taking place - rented properties are used as tourist accommodation - the purchase of village cottages as second homes reduces the available stock for local people. Tenant farmers in less-favourable areas and elderly single people dependent on a state pension also struggle with a basic existence.	- Poor quality housing - High levels of income support and other means-related benefits
Opportunity deprivation	Lack of access to education, health, work, shops, social services Rural residents travelling long distances for employment or services and/or paying higher prices in the local area.	Rural services are increasingly centralised in towns and villages to cut the cost of providing them. Some services are only supported if the threshold population is maintained. If there is out-migration then the shop, school or health care centre may close Changes in employment away from agriculture and primary industries can result in unemployment and difficulty in transferring skills Employment in 'new' sectors such as recreation and tourism and teleworking are often casual, seasonal, have low wages or have little job security.	- Distance to various services - Prices in local shops
Mobility deprivation	Lack of public transport or community buses Inability to afford a car or motor bike	Since de-regulation of the bus services in the UK, routes need to be cost-effective. Without subsidies or legislation, rural services are often the first to be reduced. A shift to a more wealthy population who use a car to commute to work or to access services encourages lack of such services to continue	- Car ownership levels - Frequency of bus services to key villages or the local town

Table 1 Types of rural deprivation

The combined impact of these different elements is the cycle of rural deprivation (see page 108) and can cause **social exclusion**, which may lead to **rural depopulation**. Changes in rural villages can generate conflicts in environments and communities. Examples include:

- second home owners and the local population
- local shop owners and larger competitors in the nearby town
- planners and local councils who are likely to control or allow development in the village and surrounding area and community groups.

Changes in a village can be examined by a range of primary fieldwork surveys such as: traffic levels and vehicle type; condition of housing; crime surveys, environmental quality surveys, residents survey (e.g. age) etc.

Initiatives in the UK to address rural deprivation and poverty

In November 2000, the British government published its second Rural White Paper; the first was in 1995. Both set out a series of strategies responding to the challenge of rural deprivation and poverty, and acknowledged that many rural parishes had issues accessing services, for example 75 per cent of parishes don't have a seven-day bus service and 91 per cent of parishes don't have a bank or building society.

Strategies were devised to seek improvements in the situation in many rural areas (see some examples of these strategies in Table 3).

Key concepts

Social exclusion: exists where certain sectors of the population are excluded from social, economic and cultural opportunities because of low income, poor health or reduced access to services.

Rural depopulation: the decrease in the population of rural areas, whether by migration or by falling birth rates as young people move away, usually to urban areas.

Issue	Examples of initiatives	Specific examples of initiatives
Housing	- Schemes to limit the purchase of houses to people who live or work in the area - Initiatives to assist rural homeless	English Villages Housing Association provided ten shared ownership houses in Ashdon, near Saffron Walden, and if sold they must go to people of the village.
Village services	- Community Services Grants (part of the Vital Villages Scheme) helps communities maintain or introduce services which are local priorities, such as a village shop or a child care scheme	Barrow Primary School in Lancashire provides activities for pupils until 5.30pm and then from 6–9pm; any pupil, ex-pupil or parent can use the computer or library facilities Suffolk ACRE Ltd (Action for Communities in Rural England) was awarded £25,000 to create a before and after school and holiday childcare scheme for children aged 3 to 5 years.
Rural transport	- Rural Transport Partnership Scheme (Vital Villages scheme) aimed at preventing the decline of rural bus services.	In rural Norfolk: - unprofitable routes are subsidised - flexible feeder projects, funded from 1998 under the Rural Bus Challenge scheme, run bus services from villages to market towns like Downham Market - Volunteer drivers provide community bus services using vehicles owned by the council
Economic activities	- Rural Development Areas (funding priority areas): grants available to aid farm diversification - Relaxed planning controls on the conversion of redundant farms for business use	North Norfolk RDA receives approx £1 m per year to tackle issues of declining farm employment, low wages and the out-migration of young people. Funded projects have developed tourism facilities at The Brecks and diversification projects in The Fens.
Environmental aspects	- Encourage the use of brownfield sites for new developments rather than the use of the countryside - Improved management and protection for areas of outstanding natural beauty - Develop safer communities	Long Mynd, Shropshire, Common Environmentally Sensitive Areas agreement aims to prevent further damage from overgrazing and to restore the moorland vegetation. Mullion, a village in Cornwall, has set up a neighbourhood wardens' scheme to reduce crime.
General	- EU funding is available through the European Regional Development Fund or other structural funds and community initiatives - To equip every local council with an Internet link	Projects in Cornwall have been targeted at training schemes, creating employment, developing small- and medium-scale businesses, community regeneration and diversification from agriculture.

Table 3 Strategies for improvement

Rural depopulation leads to **cultural erosion**: the gradual reduction in the cultural traditions of the area. This is often as a result of population turnover. For example, holiday areas such as Ynys Mon, on Anglesey, experience an in-migration of English-speaking people.

Population turnover is the change in the social and demographic composition of rural communities due to the in-migration of more affluent, car-owning, middle aged or retired people or families with children, and the out-migration of less well-off, farm workers or village-born younger people.

This can be reduced by regeneration. Today's focus for rural regeneration are market towns. These become **key settlements**: a recent planning strategy in which certain villages, often in an accessible location, become the focus for basic services in the local area. This may be at the expense of services at other nearby settlements.

Poverty in LEDCs

Much of the poverty in LEDCs occurs in rural areas. The main effects of the cycle of rural poverty in more subsistence economies comes from the inability of people to provide themselves with adequate food as well as the impact of short-term disasters such as droughts or floods.

Therefore, poverty reduction in LEDCs largely focuses on sustainable food production, agriculture and small-scale manufacturing/craft initiatives. These need to be 'pro poor', that is, they generate net benefits and opportunities for the poor rather than just expansion as a whole. Examples are shown in Table 4.

Issue	Sustainable iniatives
Food	Increasing food production which in turn will increase incomes and the number of calories consumed Safeguarding the control of farmland to allow continued production of staple crops. (The poorest groups spend almost three-quarters of their income on food, receive two-thirds of their calories from staple crops and earn half of their income from growing them)
Utilities and services	Provide electricity, services, roads and research that normally only central governments can supply Better allocation and distribution of clean water to the rural poor as more rural areas are affected by water scarcity and diversion schemes Schemes to improve rural health and literacy which often advances economic growth or makes development more likely to succeed.
Empowerment of local people	Schemes such as co-operatives to share experience, expertise or purchasing power Focus on particular groups such as women or ethnic minority groups
Employment and trade	Give the poor fair access to world markets and the ability to trade Diversification of employment into non-farm activities such as tourism, manufacturing or craft industries

Table 4 Sustainable initiatives for reducing poverty in LEDCs

Case study: South Philippines (an HEP scheme)

Background:

- The small village of Megkawayan, on Mindanao is located 50km from Davao City, 600m above sea level, in a steep mountainous area. It seems remote, has only unmade roads and few services. The electricity grid ends many kilometres away.
- Much of the population migrated to the village some 30 year ago, seeking a better life away from the rising populations and land pressures in the more urbanised areas of the lowlands. The remainder of the villagers are local people who practice slash-and-burn agriculture.

- In recent years, villagers have successfully campaigned against commercial logging and have promoted eco-friendly farming practises.

The scheme:

- A micro hydro-electric dam has been constructed on a stream which runs through the area. The land for this has been donated by a local farmer. The turbine and generating plant is on another farm, 50m downhill, and takes only a few square metres of land
- The system generates 3.5kW of power, enough to provide lighting to 80 households in the evenings and to allow corn and rice milling during the day.
- A local farmer acts as caretaker and the community organises regular voluntary maintenance of the system.
- The people are assisted by YAMOG, an alternative energy organisation based in the Philippines, and supported by Community Aid Abroad
- Local people, especially women, have formed community groups that meet to discuss ways of getting electric lighting. Local women now control the management committee of the co-operative established to administer the system. The village co-operative makes all the policies for the generation and use of electricity, including setting its own tariffs, which are put back into maintaining the system.
- The system also provides an incentive to conserve and maintain the forest cover in the water catchment area in order to preserve the supply of water to the micro-hydro.

Quick check questions

1 Outline what impact the cycle of deprivation will have on an affected village.

2 What initiatives have been used to address deprivation in a village or rural area you have studied?

3 How will the micro-hydro at Megkawayan affect the quality of life of its inhabitants?

Rural environments: Exam style questions

1. Study the table below which shows the attitude of residents towards the environment and local services along the rural-urban continuum. Figures given are the percentages of residents in each area.

Issue	Area		
	Inner urban	Suburban	Remote rural
Environmental aspects perceived as a problem:			
Crime	68	58	45
Noise	43	23	14
Traffic	55	40	32
Local services perceived as good:			
Public transport	91	83	36
Schools	79	94	91
Leisure facilities	64	64	54

    i)   Compare the changes in perceptions along the rural-urban continuum.   (4)

    ii)   Suggest reasons for the changes in perceptions between the three groups surveyed on:
- traffic
- schools.   (4)

2. Suggest some possible advantages and disadvantages of living in a more remote rural area in the UK.   (4)

3. Study Figure 1 below which shows changes in rurality with economic development.

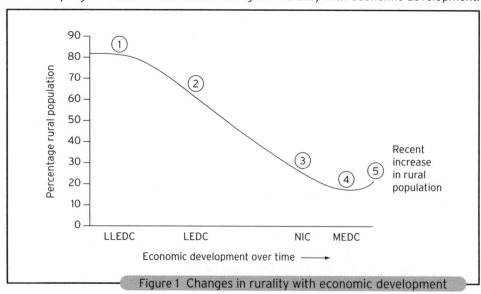

Figure 1 Changes in rurality with economic development

    i)   Suggest reasons why the percentage of population living in rural areas declines as a country develops economically.   (3)

    ii)   At stage 4 on the graph, areas can experience problems of rural depopulation.

              Explain what is meant by rural depopulation. (2)

              Outline what impact this is likely to have on the population structure of the area. (3)

4.   Study Figure 2 below which show changes in land use in a Lake District valley.

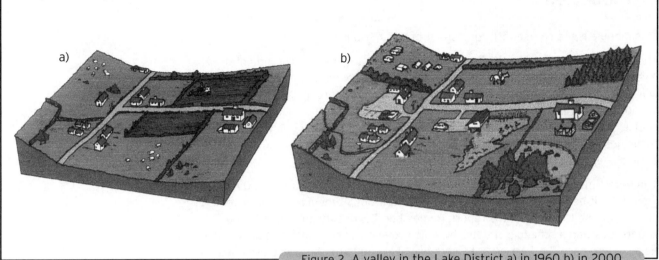

Figure 2 A valley in the Lake District a) in 1960 b) in 2000

    i)   Describe three changes that have occurred in this area between 1960 and 2000. (3)

    ii)   Outline the positive and negative impacts such changes have on rural communities. (5)

5.   Explain how population movements might influence the provision of services in a typical village in the UK. (4)

6.   With reference to a named example, explain how rural development projects can lead to changes in the lives of the rural poor in LEDCs. (6)

7.   Suggest two reasons why local rural community projects are often more effective than large-scale government schemes. (4)

8.   With reference to a named rural area, examine how decision makers have managed the consequences of either growth or decline. (10)

9.   With reference to specific examples, examine the ways in which rural environments are being modified by tourism. (10)

PART 3

The environmental investigation

Introduction

This module is the coursework component of the AS course.

The aim of this section is to assist you in producing a top grade environmental investigation report. This means ensuring that your report does justice to all the hard work that has gone into collecting data either in fieldwork groups or individually. This section therefore focuses on the production of the report rather than the initial choice of topic to investigate, any secondary data sources or any fieldwork techniques. However, there are many geography textbooks that offer advice on the early stages of fieldwork.

The report makes up 33.3 per cent of the AS marks, yet has a limit of 2500 words. Therefore, it needs to be succinct and well thought out. Remember to allow yourself sufficient time to complete the report. Remember it is quality not quantity that counts. Drafting a schedule of dates by which you should complete certain sections helps you to pace the work; your teacher will help you to do this if you are unsure of how long each section will take. Most importantly, try to stick to your plan to avoid a rush and panic as the deadline approaches.

The following sections give you:

- the criteria on which your report will be assessed
- guidance on how to complete each section of the report
- tips and advice as you go along
- information on putting your report together so that the final presentation brings it all together.

How to approach the coursework

General information

This investigative report needs to focus on an environmental question, issue or problem at a site or within a small area. A useful starting point is to examine the **assessment criteria** in detail and what is expected for each element (Table 1).

Marks available	Requirements for top band marks for each criteria
10 marks	**1 Purpose of investigation – developing a focus:** A very clear purpose with a focused statement of aims and key questions and location
15 marks	**2 Methods of data selection, collection and recording** Relevant, evidenced comprehensive data collection programme. Appropriate, accurate techniques with sound methodology. Very organised and effective presentation. Shows initiative
10 marks	**3 Data representation** Wide range of well presented, appropriate data representation
25 marks	**4 Analysis and explanation** Precise explanation, detailed analysis of all results using a range of appropriate techniques. Clear understanding of overall trends. Appropriate use of models and theories to inform data analysis.
25 marks	**5 Evaluation and conclusion** A very thorough conclusion. All aspects of the enquiry have been reviewed and evaluated in considerable detail.
15 marks	**6 Quality of written communication** A very well organised logical route to enquiry, with excellent standards of legibility, spelling, punctuation and grammar. Precise clear use of terminology. Very appropriate style of writing. N.B. If your investigation exceeds 2500 words it will gain a maximum of 6 marks for this criteria
Total marks available: 100	

Table 1 Assessment criteria

Key concept

Assessment criteria: the different aspects upon which your report is marked. Try to familiarise yourself with what is required for the upper marks in each of the categories.

Reminder

1 Look carefully at the different sections of the mark scheme and make sure that you include parts in your report to cover all sections of the assessment criteria. Very often, the conclusion is left out or inadequately written, and this section makes up 25 per cent of the total marks.
2 Remember to keep your Action Plan up to date as you complete each task. A copy will need to go into the front of the completed report. You can then also use your report as part of your Key Skills portfolio.

It might be useful to divide the report into sections that correspond to the categories in this mark scheme although data representation is likely to be integrated with the analysis. Also acknowledge all your sources of information, including any diagrams that you copy from books, Internet sites, and so on.

The remainder of this section will look at each element of the report in detail.

1 The purpose of the investigation (10 marks)

This section is the **introduction** to your report and in it you need to outline why you are doing it. Keep this section short, perhaps around 300 words, but with a detailed *annotated* sketch map of the area that you are investigating. Figure 1 on page 128 is a good example. You do not need to include more generalised maps of the county or UK.

- Provide a brief introduction to the study area, linked to your sketch map.
- You might include some annotated photographs of the location if they help in introducing a particular issue or location.

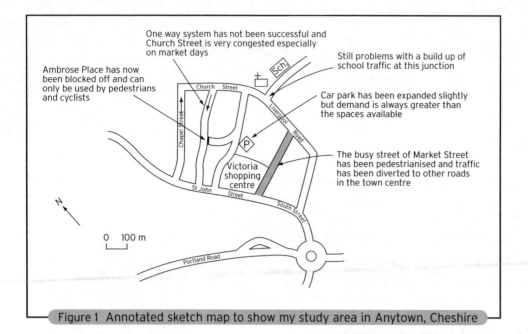

Figure 1 Annotated sketch map to show my study area in Anytown, Cheshire

- Place the investigation in its geographical context. This might be examining a particular issue or problem but it must also have clear links to the theory covered in Units 1 and 2 of the AS specification.
- Write a very clear statement of the aims of the investigation.
- Including two or three key questions too will help you to focus your study on a manageable amount of information and data for the time and words available.

An example of a project aim and key questions are given in Table 2.

Aim	To examine the success of visitor management at Dovedale, a local honeypot site
Key question 1	What evidence is there of visitor pressure in the area?
Key question 2	What is the extent of visitor management in the area?
Key question 3	To what extent does it appear that the different elements of this management strategy been successful?

Table 2

It is also useful to outline what you would expect each key question to show. An example for key question 2 above would be:

'I would expect visitor pressure to be controlled by a good standard of environmental management, due to it being a longstanding visitor attraction and there have been several phases of footpath reinforcement, vegetation replanting and car park extensions.'

2 Methodology of data selection, collection and recording (15 marks)

This section needs to be organised and relevant. Many students find that this section is best summarised in a data methodology table. Use the appendix at the back of the report to show examples of data collection evidence, for example, samples of field data recording or questionnaires. Remember, this section must not be a blow-by-blow account of a fieldtrip or just a description of what you did to collect data. If you have collected data in a group you also need to make sure that the table only relates to data that is relevant to your aim and key questions.

Reminder

Keep a record of the books, reports, newspapers and Internet sites used as you go along. This will make it easier to compile your bibliography at the end of your report.

Remember to include an outline of any sampling techniques used such as random, (e.g. using a dice), systematic, (e.g. surveying every tenth house) or representative, (e.g. asking questionnaires to people that represent different age groups). Include the reasons why different methods were appropriate in different situations. Also refer to any limitations of your data collection.

To achieve high marks in this section you need to ensure that you have a wide variety of data collection from **primary** and **secondary** sources. Also make sure that the sample size for questionnaires or other surveys is large enough for meaningful analysis.

Give an indication of which data was collected individually and which was collected by a group of students. You should also collect data yourself and show initiative such as how have you adapted or extended the group approach. Examples of this might include:

- using the group questionnaire as a pilot questionnaire which you then repeat in a different locality having amended it to solve any weak questions or to gain additional information
- adapting group recording sheets to suit your study focus
- returning to the site to collect additional data, for example, traffic counts at a different time of day or day of the week
- taking photographs or completing field sketches alongside your other data collection that shows data collection techniques or particular issues in the locality, e.g. litter or traffic levels, tourist pressure, riverbank erosion. These can then be annotated later and included in your project
- obtaining secondary information to complement your primary data collection, such as census data, a river's management plan, newspaper articles on a particular issue or government agency data on traffic flow, pollution levels, etc.

An example of a tabular methodology is given in Table 3.

Data collected	Reasons for data collected	Methodology of data collection (including sampling technique)	Equipment used	Limitations	Possible improvements

Table 3

3 Data representation (10 marks)

The key to success in this part of your study is to include a variety of data representation techniques. Take care to use the most appropriate technique for the data collected and for what you are trying to show. Aim to include at least five different techniques of data representation and analysis to give yourself the best possible chance of high marks.

Avoid basic repetitive techniques such as multiple bar charts for data representation. Figure 2 (page 130) gives some ideas of different techniques that you could use.

Consider whether you could combine different techniques, use an overlay to superimpose a second data set or for annotation, or plot two sets of data on a graph making it easier to analyse later. Remember, it is quality not quantity that is required and a single carefully constructed map or graph comparing several sets of information will achieve higher marks than several pages of pie charts showing individual site information.

Remember that if you are comparing data you need to use the same technique to make this process easier. Avoid representing the same data in various ways; you will not score any additional marks for doing this.

Reminder

You could include small photographs, annotated maps and/or diagrams to show how data was collected. Photographs could also be used to illustrate a scale, (e.g. of housing quality) to show the standard linked to particular ratings.

Key concepts

Primary data: data that has been recorded directly by you as part of fieldwork or a visit to a particular site.
Secondary data: this comes from another source such as a book, report, Internet site, television programme, etc. All secondary sources must be acknowledged in your study. Any diagrams used directly in sections of your report should have their source written below. This will then need to link to a full reference in the bibliography at the back of the report.

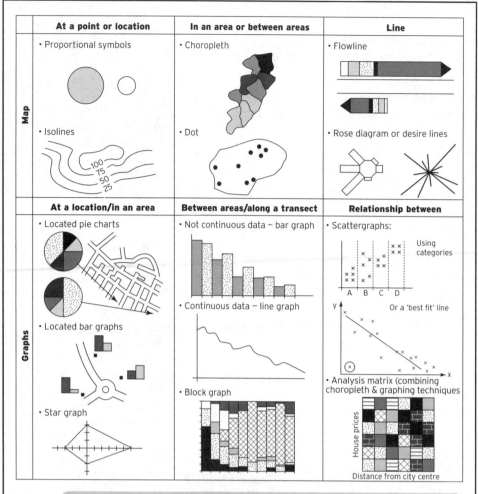

Figure 2 Examples of some key presentation and analysis techniques

Reminder

As well as a contents list, include a figures list at the beginning of your project. This should be one of your last tasks when putting your project together.

Give all maps, tables, graphs and diagrams a figure number and refer to them in the text. Integrate photographs into the text of the investigation rather than keeping them in a separate section. Computer-generated maps, graphs and diagrams can be included but carefully hand drawn ones can achieve as many marks.

Also, remember to evaluate the techniques used either in this section of the report or in the conclusion and evaluation section later on.

4 Analysis and explanation (25 marks)

This is your opportunity to interpret your results, so make sure that you both describe in detail *and* analyse your results. Put linked data together to get an overview rather than a blow-by-blow account. Include a paragraph to show any overall trends and patterns too.

This section is worth 25 per cent of the total marks and is often what shows the difference between an average project and a good one. You should aim to write at least 900 words in this section and include some written commentary as well as analysis graphs, tables, statistics, etc.

Select appropriate statistical techniques to look at any correlations. Show that you understand the appropriateness and limitations of the techniques used. Examples of possible statistical techniques are shown in Table 4.

Reminder

Use dividers in your working folder to organise your draft write-up and to keep graphs, maps, diagrams, in the correct section. This also highlights any sections which have very little in them. If you are only using a computer and scanning in diagrams etc., using different folders within your overall project file produces the same result.

Task	Examples	Statistical test
Analysing data at a point or in an area	What is the mean velocity in the upper section of the stream?	Mean (average) Median Mode (most common)
	To what extent do visitor facilities cluster around the redeveloped docks area of the city centre?	Nearest neighbour analysis
Comparing the frequency (numbers) in different categories	Is the population structure of the study area the same as the city as a whole?	Chi-squared test
	Do particular species of caterpillar prefer to feed on particular dune plant species?	
Finding if there is a difference between two averages	Is there, on average, a higher species diversity in the dunes than in the slack areas?	Wilcoxon signed rank or Mann-Whitney U test
	Is there a difference in stream velocity in the riffle and pool sections of the stream?	t-test
Investigating the relationship between two variables	Is there a relationship between distance from the shopping centre and pedestrian flows?	Spearman's Rank or Pearson's Product Moment
	Do pollution levels vary with distance from the road?	Regression analysis (often in conjunction with a scattergraph)

Table 4 Example of statistical techniques

Make sure that any analysis fits the original hypothesis and key questions so that all the work that you are doing is directly relevant. In fact, it is often useful to analyse the data under each of the key questions in turn if the structure of your project allows this. This will mean that the data is analysed in a logical and methodical way.

To achieve more than 10 out of the 25 marks available you must show accurate and detailed knowledge of the relevant theory by comparing your results to models and theories that have been taught in Units 1 and 2. Integrate this with the data analysis.

5 Evaluation and conclusion (25 marks)

To achieve high marks you need to make sure that you cover both aspects in this section. Once again, this section is worth 25 per cent of the total marks for your project, so you should be allocating around 700 words for this section. Just as importantly, you should make sure that you leave yourself sufficient time to do it justice. All too often, students rush this section or leave it incomplete, which reflects in the final coursework mark.

In the conclusion, summarise and draw threads together. Refer back to your data collection and analysis and summarise your findings and linkage to theory or models. Re-state your original project aim and key questions and highlight what your research has shown. If you devised a hypothesis as part of your introduction, return to it. To what extent was it proved correct? If not, what other factors may have affected the result. Alternatively, has your project suggested an alternative pattern or hypothesis? Better projects refer back to specific maps and figures in earlier sections so that the whole investigation is well integrated.

To extend your conclusion, link your results to their wider geographical context, i.e. do the patterns shown by your results fit in with existing theory or models or are there different reasons for your results? What implications do your results have for the future, for anyone else's research, or for the management of your study area?

Reminder

Choice of graph Take care when using Excel to get the right choice of graphs. For example, to obtain a best fit line on a graph comparing two sets of data, select the scattergraph option initially.
Timing Draw all your maps, graphs, and diagrams and then write the analysis; this takes a lot of time compared with other sections of the project.

Reminder

Use of statistics Marks are only awarded for an appropriate, (i.e. correct), use of statistics. Firstly, check that you have sufficient data to make the results of any statistical test valid. Also do not just use a technique because you know it well. It might not be the best one for the data in your investigation or for what you are trying to compare.
Prose vs. tables Using tables for both the analysis and concluding sections of the report is not a good idea. Investigations that contain little written prose tend not to compare trends and draw threads together across all of the results. Such reports therefore often do not achieve top marks in each category.

For the evaluation element, use different types of evaluative techniques. Again show individuality. Some suggestions include:

- SWOT-style analysis, where you examine the strengths and weaknesses of the methods and techniques used in your investigation together with their limitations and opportunities for further investigation
- using different colours to highlight strengths and weaknesses
- tabular approaches showing strengths against weaknesses also work well
- force-field analysis, where the size of the arrow representing a strength or a weakness is linked to how significant that point is.

6 Quality of written communication (15 marks)

Marks are awarded in this section for more than just spelling and presentation. Remember to be precise and succinct, make every word count. Make sure that the grammar and punctuation are correct and the report reads fluently. Organise the information into a logical and coherent report divided up into clear sections that has page numbers. It must also have a contents page at the front. Word process your report, unless you have special permission not to, and check that the style (font and size), is consistent throughout. Assemble the report in a lightweight folder with your completed and signed action plan at the front. Only use plastic wallets for fragile or complex materials.

Throughout your report ensure that you:

- use geographical terminology to show a knowledge of key processes and concepts, but make sure you are using them in the correct context
- link back to geographical theory covered in Units 1 and 2 wherever possible in the analysis of your data
- precisely label all maps, diagrams and photos, check they have a scale, a key etc, and link to the relevant section in the text
- incorporate diagrams, graphs, photographs into the written report at the relevant point rather than clustering them together in separate sections
- acknowledge the sources of all diagrams, maps and photographs taken from secondary sources such as books, Internet sites, journals; the full reference can then be included in the bibliography at the back of the report
- evaluate across each of the report sections, for example, the data collection methods, data representation techniques, the results gained compared with accepted theory, and of the completion of the overall project.

Use accepted conventions for the bibliography and include any websites.

Books and reports: Author's surname and initials; date of publication and any edition number; *title of publication*; publisher's name

Newspapers: date of the article and the *name of the newspaper*; page reference (if you have it)

Internet sources: *website address*; if a report can be viewed from a website then include its reference, if known, in the usual way (see books and reports above)

Reminder

Proof reading Some students ask a relative or friend to proof read the report to make sure that it makes sense to another reader.

What an appendix should show

- sample evidence of data collection, including any individual work
- directly relevant secondary information.

Do not include whole reports or all of your questionnaires since it makes the report too bulky. Graphs or tables that are referred to in the main text of the report should not go into the appendix.

General presentation tips

- Use A4 paper and avoid too many A3 fold-outs.
- Word process your report unless you have permission not to, but remember to save a copy on disk.
- Check ICT formats, font type, sizes for headings etc., to adopt a style throughout.
- Assemble in a lightweight folder and only use plastic wallets for fragile or complex material.
- Organise the information into a clear and logical report divided up into obvious sections.
- Incorporate a Contents page and a Bibliography, including websites.
- Appendix: include sample evidence of data collection techniques and it should include evidence of individual work.
- Acknowledgement of all sources.
- Include a copy of the Action Plan at the front of the report.

The last thing to remember when completing your report is to build into your schedule sufficient time for the final compilation of the report. Allow at least a day for checking (spell check, putting in figure numbers, scales, tidying up shading, index, bibliography, etc.) **Make sure that you have a back-up copy on a disc to guard against any printing problems as the deadline approaches.** Give yourself enough time to print out the final copy and to assemble the finished product, and do not underestimate the time it will take you to do this!

Answers to exam questions

When you start to answer exam questions, think 'a mark a minute'. In fact, you might want to practise answering some of the questions in a given time limit.

There are different styles of exam question at AS Level. The exam question sections in this book include a mixture of these different styles.

1. Data response questions that use a resource as a stimulus
2. Short answer questions
3. Extended questions which are allocated 10 marks out of the total of 30 marks for each question. In the answer booklet, 30 lines are allocated for an extended question although you can use additional space at the rear of the booklet to continue. This means that your answer to this style of question needs to be fact-packed and focused on the key elements of the question. You cannot afford time to waffle. These 'mini essay' questions are marked using what is known as a levels mark scheme. An example is given below.

9–10 marks (Level 3)	A well structured balanced account that looks at a range of aspects. It contains detailed reference to relevant case study information. Shows clear focus on the question.
5–8 marks (Level 2)	An account with some structure that focuses on several aspects. May not be balanced but has some references to examples.
1–4 marks (Level 1)	One or two basic suggestions. Likely to be generalised with little or no reference to any examples

Reading a question carefully will give you clues as to what is expected for the top level. All the extended questions will expect case study detail to be included.

River environments exam questions answers

1. i)   A drainage basin is an area of land (or catchment) drained by a river and its tributaries. Its boundary is marked by a ridge of high land (the watershed) outside of which any precipitation will drain into neighbouring basins.
    ii) Base flow is discharge or flow from groundwater sources, often known as 'normal' flow and not that from storms.
    iii) Saturated overland flow occurs when the water table reaches the surface and the ground becomes totally saturated, i.e. pore spaces in the soil become full of water. As a result, any runoff will be on the surface.
    iv) River competence is the diameter of the largest particle that can be carried by a river at a particular time or location.
    v)   River regime is the seasonal variation in the flow of a river, usually over the period of a year. A river regime hydrograph shows its mean monthly discharge figures against time; any variation results from its response to the region's climate.
    For each above answer, 2 marks would be available for a full definition. A partial idea would gain 1 mark.

2. A closed system is where there is a constant cycling of water and although the water may change form, for example from liquid to vapour, there is no loss of water from the cycle.

3. Braiding (when a river splits into many channels) tends to occur when:
   - the river has a large load
   - the discharge is variable (and therefore its capacity to carry sediment varies) for example, due to seasonal rainfall or snowmelt
   - the banks are made of material that easily erodes
   - a river level falls rapidly, reducing river competence and capacity and choking the channel with material.

4. A change from woodland to agriculture results in the removal of trees and an increase in grazing land and/or arable crops. Therefore, there is likely to be less interception, more surface flow, faster runoff and increased discharge. In terms of quality, there would be less filtering, more erosion of sediments plus a possible increase in the use of farm chemicals/fertilisers which may increase pollution and decrease discharge quality. This may even lead to eutrophication.

5. Waterfalls frequently occur on horizontally bedded rocks.
   - The soft rock is undercut by hydraulic action and abrasion.
   - The weight of the water and the lack of support cause the waterfall to collapse.
   - After collapse, some of the rock will be swirled around by the river, especially during times of high discharge, to form a deep plunge pool.
   - Over thousands of years this process is repeated many times causing the waterfall to produce headward retreat, (i.e. up the river).
   - This may form a gorge of recession. An example of this is Niagara Falls, which retreats by 1 metre per year.
   - Rapids occur where the layers of hard and soft rock are very thin and so no obvious break of slope develops as a waterfall.

6. This question relates to managing water supply at different locations. For example, in the Murray Darling River in south-eastern Australia, there is often an imbalance between water demand and supply. Increased demand is due to the rapid growth of key cities in the region, irrigation of the demanding arable farms in the locality, HEP developments and a water transfer system. Water supply is governed by seasonal rainfall (May–October maximum; lowest in January) and high evaporation rates in the summer months. Tributaries supply the south of the catchment with seasonal snowmelt discharge.

   In Bangladesh, in the wet season, flooding is widespread, although there have been some attempts recently to control this using embankments. However, at other times, there is much less water available; construction of the Farakka Dam in India leaves only one-third of the normal river flow in the Bangladesh section of the River Ganges which may hinder irrigation, fishing and navigation in some areas.

7. i) Peak discharge = 22 cumecs; lag time (i.e. the difference between peak rainfall and peak discharge) = 5 hours
   ii) Lag time is the delay between rain falling on the ground or being intercepted by vegetation, and it reaching the gauging station in the river. This will be longer if water infiltrates below ground and flows to the river channel as throughflow.
   iii) The hydrograph for river P has a shorter lag time (1.5 hours compared with 5 hours for river Q). Also, river P has a higher peak discharge (37 cumecs compared with 22 cumecs for river Q).
   iv) Possible reasons include land use and slope gradient. There are steep slopes in the upper reaches of river P, which will increase the speed of any runoff from these areas into the river channel. Land use in river P's catchment is largely arable with some pasture. This means that the density and height of ground cover vegetation will be less than in the dense woodland that makes up the majority of the catchment area of river Q. Therefore interception will also be lower in catchment P. Arable farming in P may also be seasonal which will further affect vegetation cover and may also be affected by farming practices such as watering or irrigation.

v)   Enlarging village A into a new town will increase the number of impermeable surfaces in the catchment as well as developing more efficient ways for water to reach the river channel, e.g. through drains. As a result on the hydrograph, the rising and falling limbs are likely to become steeper, the lag time will be reduced and peak discharge will be higher. Sediment levels during the initial construction phases will be increased as surface material is disturbed. Once completed, the reduced amount of open space within the town will provide fewer sources of sediment, although there may be knock-on effects elsewhere in the catchment area that may offset this effect.

8.   The increase in velocity may be due a larger hydraulic radius, a smoother cross-section and less turbulence, despite gentler downstream gradient.
     The increase in discharge may be due to an increase in volume from tributaries joining the main river channel, greater area of catchment, larger cross-section to carry water and increased velocity.

9.   i)   Sand
     ii) Gravel
     There is a change to deposition as the river velocity falls below the critical settling velocity for particular sizes of sediment. Gravel is deposited first (starting when the river velocity falls below approx 85 cm/sec), followed by sand after it falls to around 25 cm/sec and then silt below 4 cm/sec. Clay stays in transport as it is held in suspension.

10. Two possible examples that could form a focus for this question could be:
     - channel improvements and embankments in Keswick, UK, together with regular inspections of the defences and controls on future building on the floodplain area (see pages 28–33 of *Changing Environments*, Heinemann 2000)
     - the use of dams (hard engineering) such as the Tiga Dam, and the Nguru wetlands conservation project (soft engineering) in the Komadugu-Yobe river basin in NE Nigeria (see page 41).

11. Wetlands are important in river management since peatlands can store water quickly but release it slowly. They also have a role in pollution control since wetland plants and bacteria trap and breakdown sewage and farm runoff. Such strategies are known as soft engineering. A plan to conserve the Nguru Wetlands area in NE Nigeria resulted in the maintenance of the buffer zone against the intense tropical rains and associated flooding between June and August. Alongside this, the scheme also taught local people about wetland management and the maintenance of marsh grazing.
     In the Kissimee River in Florida, USA sections of flood control canal are being dismantled to restore an area of wetland with a more natural seasonal pattern of high and low flows in the river. This work started in 1999 and is likely to take 15 years to complete. Channel vegetation has already started to return and water quality is improving as well as acting as a more sustainable strategy for managing flood risk in the surrounding area.

Coastal environments exam questions answers

1.   i)   A = headland; B = bay, beach or a cove; C = spit
     ii) This question expects a comparison between aspects of the two cliffs. This could include height (8m vs 15m), steepness (gentle vs almost vertical), profile (stepped vs smooth) and geology (unconsolidated boulder clay vs horizontal strata of sandstone and coal seam topped by boulder clay).
     iii) Possible effects include more cliff erosion, loss of beaches, more sediment in the river estuary plus the possible growth of the spit due to the unhindered transport of sediment along the coast by longshore drift.

2. The coast is an open system since at any one location there are inputs and outputs. Inputs include water and sediment from river estuaries, marine deposition from off-shore locations, and via mass movement and subaerial processes operating on coastal cliffs. Water is also transported out to the offshore area and sediment may be deposited as sand banks. Deposition of sediment also takes place on shore as aeolian (wind blown) deposits, within river mouths or to form sand dunes. The action of longshore drift produces both inputs and outputs to a locality. Human activity, such as dredging or the removal of cliff top vegetation, can also affect the coastal system.

3. Short-term flooding usually affects the coastal plain region and result from tidal surges or is associated with cyclone activity. Longer-term strategies focus on rising sea levels. Responses to a flood risk might include the use of embankments (e.g. Bangladesh), barrages on major rivers, (e.g. River Thames Barrier), and sea walls, (e.g. Netherlands). A more recent approach is to allow managed retreat, i.e. no defences are used or existing ones are dismantled on stretches of coastline that have low-value land use.

4. i) Offshore bars deflect storm waves and prevent beach erosion. The beach was built up by nourishment to reduce any affects of erosion. The rock groynes are designed to combat longshore drift and prevent beach erosion. The beach protects the sea wall from toe erosion thereby protecting the high value town area.

   ii) The rock groynes prevent east–west longshore drift which could lead to sediment starvation at Pennington Point, therefore leaving the headland unprotected from marine attack.

   Tourism could be affected by the issue of beach access, the unsightly nature and smell of the rock armour and the rock groynes or the nature of the offshore bars/breakwaters at low tide. The shingle beach may not appeal to some visitors either.

5. A fresh supply of sand (bought onshore by constructive waves); a frequent onshore wind direction to blow the sediment; a macro tidal environment to give a wide, dry beach; vegetation to trap the sand to give it stability to increase; and protection from storms and other damaging activity.

6. Plant succession is the process by which vegetation develops as it colonises areas and becomes increasingly adapted to the environment. This process makes up a psammosere. Each stage is a sere. There is initial colonisation by pioneer vegetation species of the bare sand. These gradually modify the environment so new plants become established especially in the lee (down-wind) side. As dunes become older and more protected from the strength of the on-shore breezes and soil conditions become less alkaline, with more humus content, soil depth and water availability, plant communities become increasingly diverse and complex. Because of arresting factors such as human influence, climatic climax vegetation often does not develop. Dune heath (sub climax) or planted conifers (plagioclimax) is more usual. An example of sand dune succession is Studland Heath with foredune vegetation of sea couch grass developing to marsh plants and willow further into the dunes (see page 54). There is also a difference between the vegetation of the more exposed sea-facing slopes of the dune and that found on the lee side of the dune or in the wetter dune slacks.

7. i) 1 Recurved sea wall; 2 Rock armour or rip-rap; 3 Gabion or gabion cage
   ii) Answer is likely to focus on strengths and weaknesses but could also include some discussion of how well a design works in practice. For example, you could set up a table to show design strengths and weaknesses (see over).

Methods	Design strengths	Practical weaknesses
1 Recurved sea wall	Curve deflects wave energy upwards, foundations resist wave energy, height prevents erosion and flooding	Can be undermined (basal scour), needs expensive repairs, visually unattractive. (Continue)

Example table

8. Conflicts arise when there are different demands placed on an area of coastline or where developers and conservationists clash on the future management of an area. Likely examples to focus your answer on are the Dorset coastline, and/or the Ban Don Bay coral reef area in Thailand (page 64). Conflicts are likely to be between users of the Dorset coast, e.g. power-boat enthusiasts versus sailing boats; water skiing versus swimming. Concerns over the impact of tourism development and the threat to the coral reef at Ban Don Bay cause conflicts between visitors and conservationists, but there are also issues of intensive local fishing and pollution from urban and industrial areas that conflict with the preservation of the reefs.

9. Managing erosion involves analysing whether cliff face or cliff foot processes are taking place, the speed of erosion and also a cost-benefit analysis. Managing longshore drift is important when looking to place groynes otherwise there will just be knock-on erosion effects along the coast. Managing deposition is important when creating marsh areas, preserving sand dunes and in managed retreat schemes and will require an understanding of depositional processes and succession. Examples to support the main arguments could include the south Northumberland coastal area with its differences in geology and patterns of longshore drift, as well as land use affecting the management strategy at different locations. A contrasting example could be sand dune development and succession at Studland Heath, Dorset (page 55).

10. Global warming will lead to thermal expansion of oceans and the melting of ice caps in Antarctica leading to a eustatic rise in sea level. This will lead to a flooding of lowland areas such as Eastern England, the Netherlands or Bangladesh (80 per cent of the latter is delta area liable to flooding). Many of these areas are highly populated. It could also lead to the drowning of coral atoll such as the Maldives. Global warming can lead to more extreme weather and increased incidence of tropical storms which will lead to escalating coastal erosion on sensitive coasts. Higher water temperatures will cause surface expansion again leading to higher water levels and flooding. Increased carbon dioxide would make shallow water more acidic which will have an impact on coastal ecosystems. It will also cause bleaching and the death of coral reefs. It may lead to more frequent El Niño effects. The question asks for named examples and any answer must include facts and figures of relevant impact case studies to gain maximum marks. Examples might include possible impacts to the coastal barrier islands in North Carolina (page 61), the Bangladesh delta (pages 67–8) and the Ban Don Bay coral reefs, Thailand.

Urban environments exam questions answers

1. i) Marks would be awarded for highlighting trends and supporting data. For example, Inner London increases from 1m in 1801 to a peak of 4.6m in 1901, followed by a decline to 2.2m in 1981. Thereafter there is a slight increase again to 3.8m by 2001. The population for Outer London starts at a lower level initially (0.1m in 1801). After 1861, there is a relatively rapid rise to a

peak of 4.9m in 1951. This then decreases slightly to 4.1m in 1991. After that there has been a slight increase again to 4.4m in 2001.

ii) Urbanisation: reasons for this include industrialisation, the 'pull' of city life and the 'push' that causes people to leave rural areas
Suburbanisation or decentralisation: reasons for this include desire for an improved quality of life, cheaper mortgages coinciding with improved wage levels, growth of the city and suburbs with the expansion of the underground network, demolition of inner city slums and the relocation to outer housing estates.

2   i) Numbers increase from 8 in 1950 to 36 in 2000 to 52 in 2015. There has been a shift in distribution. The original focus was in Western Europe and this has gradually spread across developing countries. The hub is now in South and South East Asia.

ii) Early development of cities in the MEDCs especially in Western Europe occurred with the Industrial Revolution and the development of secondary industry. At this time, LEDCs still focused on an agricultural economy. Between 1950 and 2000, cities have gradually grown due to rural-urban migration, push and pull factors and the global shift in industry. Between 2000 and 2015, it can be expected that this shift will continue with the further development of certain LEDC cities due to being financial, service or manufacturing centres.

3. i) Likely to be at 400 metres since all land use until then is CBD functions, with limited open space and no residential land use.

ii) The main factor is the cost of land with retail 'out-bidding' other land uses in the high-value CBD (according to the bid rent theory). Other factors could include the nature of demands for a particular type of land, e.g. high quality residential areas could be linked to open spaces.

4. Characteristics might include high pedestrian flows; predominant land use of retail and offices; high building height; high traffic flows; parking restrictions; pedestrianisation; high building density.

5. Points might include pull factors such as the availability of a larger site; improved accessibility; space for parking; proximity to the customers, or push factors such as traffic congestion and a lack of space.

6. Advantages include planned land use often with housing being separate from industry, relieves population pressure on the main city and designed to give better living conditions. Disadvantages include a biased population structure in the early phase (towards young employed people). People may still return to the main city for many functions rather than use the new development services initially. Examples of new towns are Milton Keynes in the UK and the Tenth of Ramadan for Cairo, Egypt.

7. Help to regenerate the CBD might include a new residential area to bring young, higher-earning residents back to the city; a new business park to attract investment; a cosmopolitan atmosphere created by improved restaurants, bars, etc; a ring road to divert through traffic around the centre; pedestrianisation to make a safer environment; improved public transport links with the new bus station, and a possible park and ride.

8. Rural-urban fringes in LEDCs often contain unplanned settlements (shanty developments), poor quality housing and quality of life, limited services/utilities, possibly new town developments, possibly pockets of high class residential associated with a commercial spine or main routeway. In MEDCs the focus is on suburban housing (generally middle- to higher-class housing or large estates of local authority housing), transport routes such as a by-pass or ring road, green spaces, industrial areas (often light industry close to main routes), out-of-town retail areas, greenbelt land.

9. Improvements may focus on empowering low-income households and communities to organise improvements (i.e. self help schemes), for example, Lima or Bangkok; sustainable investment programmes in services and utilities; recycling programmes, for example, Zabbaleen in Cairo; provision of low-cost housing or even new town developments; programmes to reduce pollution levels and/or plans to restrict emissions and traffic levels, for example, Bangkok.

10. Cities could be made more sustainable by the use of renewable supplies of energy, e.g. windfarms for Californian cities; the use of CHP – combined heat and power – stations, e.g. St Petersburg; use of recycling systems, e.g. Zabaleen of Cairo; use of ecofarms or city farms to supply food to city and recycle city waste, e.g. Beijing; use of composting systems (waste to feed city farms), e.g. Nairobi; reduction of pollution by a whole series of measures, e.g. electric buses in Curitiba; developing a more compact city and encouraging a revitalisation of the inner city to reduce urban sprawl and commuting distance, e.g initiatives started in Los Angeles.

Rural environments exam questions answers

1. i) In terms of local services, there is a general decrease in the percentage of residents perceiving it as good for public transport (91 per cent to 36 per cent) and leisure services (64 per cent to 54 per cent). Schools are highest in the suburbs (94 per cent) with a decrease towards rural (91 per cent) and the inner urban (79 per cent). There is also a general decrease in perceived environmental problems from inner urban to remote rural, e.g. noise (a decrease of 29 per cent) and traffic (decreased by 23 per cent).

   ii) Traffic – perceptions will be influenced by congestion and traffic levels in the inner urban areas, the proximity of major roads to suburban residential areas and any traffic management schemes. Remote rural areas will perceive traffic as less of an issue as there is less traffic in this area and no congestion problems.

   Perceptions of schools will reflect the number and proximity to different types of schools especially in rural areas and the reputation of individual schools. It may also reflect parental support for education. Inner city areas may have problems with insufficient investment and facilities to cope with social issues.

2. Advantages: 'peace and tranquility' of the countryside, community spirit, lower crime rates, better quality of life than central urban areas, space for children to play, services.
   Disadvantages: remote location with poor accessibility, dependent on agriculture or subsidies, lack of services, isolated communities, ageing population as a result of out-migration.

3. i) Essentially, migration from rural to urban areas is a result of pull and push factors (primarily greater economic opportunities). As migrants are usually of reproductive age this has the impact of slowing down the rate of natural increase in rural areas relative to urban areas.

   ii) Rural depopulation is when the out migration of people from rural areas leads to a net loss of people as the birth replacements are insufficient to replace the losses by death / out migration. Absolute depopulation occurs when the population falls below this replacement threshold.
   Ageing society (towards 65–69); few old people move out but there is outmigration of 25–29 and 30–34. This gives a wasting effect at middle age. There is a regressive base (0–4) as there are few births because of the out migration.

4 i)   Changes include: change of farm and outbuildings to holiday flats/houses; formation of a camping and caravan site; building of visitor attractions/facilities, e.g. tea shop/craft centre; pony trekking centre; restoration of heather moorland; farmhouse now offering B&B; conifers planted for alternative income; increase in vacant buildings.

   ii) Positive impacts: increase in income/alternative income source to that gained from farming; prevents dereliction of farm buildings; may generate more employment to counterbalance losses from the original farm. Negative impacts: increase in traffic, noise, pollution, etc; skills required for the 'new jobs' may not be compatible with ex-farm workers.

5.   This could involve growth and/or decline. Decline is usually associated with an ageing population which will pose difficulties for provision of most public and private services. It may mean additional strain on healthcare services if an elderly population remains. A general reduction in numbers will lead to a decline in shops, banks etc due to high cost.

   The growth of more accessible villages raises issues of affordable housing, pressure on local services such as schools and doctors because of many young families. Some services such as pubs and supermarkets could become over used but newcomers usually commute and use market town services.

6   Rural development projects could include: micro-hydro schemes, e.g. in Nepal; knitting co-operatives in Peru to give better facilities and community spirit and bring more prosperity; ecotourism, e.g. Costa Rica or Kenya, to provide increased income, employment and involvement in the development of their area; agricultural projects such as soil conservation techniques, new crop varieties, new cultivation techniques to give an increase in productivity, food supply and people's health, e.g. goat schemes in Ethiopia.

7.   Possible reasons include: less expensive, has the support of the local community, more in line with community needs and/or the level of technology available, more immediate feedback of the benefits/money to the local people. Large-scale projects may produce a leakage of funds if MEDC companies are used, possible corruption in local or central government and they may try to spread funds too thinly across a wide area making them ineffective.

8.   Answer needs to focus on either growth or decline.
   Managing growth might focus on issues of counter-urbanisation, increase in commuting traffic, conflict between locals and newcomers, development of recreation or tourism, development of resources. *Managing decline* might focus on issues of declining agriculture, lack of employment, out-migration, reducing incomes, poverty, dereliction, decrease in services and general quality of life.

9.   Modifications might include changing village communities, services and access roads developed with newcomers moving in, a switch from agriculture as part of diversification, management schemes to address the possible negative impacts around honeypot sites (e.g. litter bins, building additional car parks, traffic flow schemes). However, the development of ecotourism may have minimum impact on the environment.

Quality of written communication

AS exam papers are also assessed overall for the quality of written communication. There are up to 4 marks available for each of the papers (6471 and 6472). This is not just spelling, punctuation and grammar, it also reflects the use of geographical terminology in your answers and how clearly and fluently you express your answers.

Index

Page numbers in *italic* refer to Figures and Tables

 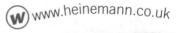